From Clinic to Corner Office

Organization and Management on the Exam Table

BY MITCHELL T. RABKIN, M.D.

For Anne,

With best wishes,

Mitch

DORRANCE
PUBLISHING CO
EST. 1920
PITTSBURGH, PENNSYLVANIA 15238

Dorrance Publishing Co
585 Alpha Drive
Suite 103
Pittsburgh, PA 15238
Visit our website at *www.dorrancebookstore.com*

ISBN: 978-1-6366-1406-9
eISBN: 978-1-6366-1982-8

COMMENTS FOR THE BOOK

"Dynamics of the academic medical center are complex. Attention to operational detail, respect for tradition, celebration of employees, success in care/education/research, and leadership reminded me why I joined Beth Israel. Dr. Rabkin makes vivid much of the history and culture so important to its institutional identity."

John D. Halamka MD, MS
President, Mayo Clinic Platform
Michael D. Brennan MD, President's Strategic Initiative Professor

Formerly, Chief Information Officer, BIDMC, and
International Healthcare Innovation Professor, Harvard Medical School

"There is much wisdom here. Dr Rabkin has written an important book on effective management drawing on more than three decades of experience as a thoughtful CEO. He combines the telling of fascinating stories with a thorough understanding of the literature on organizational effectiveness, resulting in a valuable guide for leaders across all sectors of our economy."

Robert B. McKersie, MBA, DBA, Society of Sloan Fellows Professor (Emeritus), Massachusetts Institute of Technology

"Being a nurse at Beth Israel was transformative. As a new graduate, I could sense momentum and possibilities under the leadership of Mitch Rabkin and Joyce Clifford. We were expected to be scientific and analytic in the context of our caring mission as nurses. I loved it and thrived there."

Terry Fulmer, PhD, RN, FAAN, President, John A. Hartford Foundation.

Formerly, Distinguished Professor and Dean, Bouve College of Health Sciences, Northeastern University; previously, Elaine Perkins McGriff Professor of Nursing and founding Dean, New York University College of Nursing.

"During my years training and on staff at Beth Israel, I felt part of a family, a supportive group of physicians, nurses, administrators, even kitchen, lab and housekeeping staff dedicated to the patient and each other. At its center was Mitch Rabkin, a thoughtful, caring and visionary leader dedicated to excellence. His insights into creating and maintaining a high-performing organization are indispensable not just for hospital chiefs but anyone entrusted with leadership of a complex organization."

John W. Rowe, MD

Former CEO, Mount Sinai Medical Center and School of Medicine; Former Chairman and CEO, Aetna, Inc.

"An engaging book that chronicles how this physician-teacher-leader's experience informed his journey as a successful CEO. Offering real life reflections and anecdotes, it shares valuable insights illuminating how Dr. Rabkin led Beth Israel Hospital to become one of the leading academic medical centers in the world. As a young hospital executive who learned and incorporated so many of his principles, values, role modeling and actions, I attribute the accomplishments and joy of my own leadership journey to this remarkable physician CEO."

Sandra L. Fenwick
Chief Executive Officer
Boston Children's Hospital

Readable and comprehensive, Dr. Rabkin's reflections focus on human aspects of change management and its imparting of values as a key CEO role. Incidents recalled from his distinguished career provide thought-provoking examples useful not only to CEOs and physician leaders but to managers everywhere.

Joanne Marqusee
Chief Integration Officer, *wellforce*
Formerly, President/CEO, Cooley Dickinson Health Care Corp.

CONTENTS

PREFACE

Trained in academic medicine and untutored in management, at age thirty-five, I became CEO of a major academic teaching hospital affiliated with Harvard Medical School, moving it over three decades to increasing national prominence and creating for employees what many claimed as the best working experience of their lives. A novice, I was clueless to the points later made by Laura Avakian, who joined me in 1980, outstandingly to head Human Resources.

"Physicians appointed to management roles for the first time face even greater complexity in establishing effective working relationships with both physicians and other staff who report to them. It is not uncommon for (administrative) staff to look at doctors as a kind of fraternity...their strongest bonds appear to be with each other. Other clinical, administrative, and service personnel may be intimidated by them... (And) in their relationships with each other, doctors are typically collegial and accustomed to conferring with each other...When a peer physician suddenly appears to start telling another what to do, the fraternal bond may be painfully severed." [1] I benefited from insights, coaching and tutoring generously given by a variety of hospital col-

---

[1] Avakian L. Helping Physicians Become Great Managers and Leaders. Chicago: Health Forum, Inc., American Hospital Association, 2011

leagues, administrative and medical, mentors on the hospital board and external, and from writers on organization and management. All helped me evolve from clinician-scientist, responsible to individual patients, to become a clinician-manager committed to benefit a hospital with its affiliated medical school, its patients, medical staff, employees, trustees, volunteers, supporters, and community.

I worked to educate all about the hospital's mission, its goals and its mandate — how we carry out that mission. One key is "transparency" but not unidirectional and only from top down. No one knows his or her job better than the one doing it, and to ignore views of workers at any level is to denigrate them and their roles; they are more committed, engaged, and effective when they are informed about and feel meaningful parts of the organization's mission and work. Candid feedback from subordinates is critical, and timely responses by management equally so. Top management must be open, accessible, willing to listen, consider new facts and insights, admit error, and make changes as needed. I found at all levels a commonality of commitment shared among workers supporting our concept of the "Beth Israel Family."

This book offers ways of understanding the nature of organizations, their sociology, and management. Its intended audience goes beyond hospital administrators to include managers in any organization, non-profit or for-profit. Managers and would-be managers at any level might benefit from its insights. Boards of trustees or directors, too, might be helped to meet more effectively their governance responsibilities.

INTRODUCTION

This is not a set of reminiscences; it's about organizations and their management. You might be a chief executive officer or manager at any level in any organization, non-profit or for-profit. Or you might want to be. If you have the title of *manager*, it's because the work for which you are accountable is more than you can do yourself. You are given specific authority to assign part of that work to others subordinate and accountable to you. It has nothing to do with "style." Getting work done in an organization has to do with understanding what work really is and the roles and relationships that enable work effectively to get done. That paves the way for both managers and subordinates to perform effectively.

What follows is an examination of work, its challenges, and opportunities. Partly out of my experience as a physician responsible for the care of patients, I differ from the approach of many writers on management. Most people learning to drive a car will begin reviewing how one actually drives the car — starting it, turning corners, parking, etc. That's reasonable because actions taken at the driver's seat lead to known and expected responses by the car. The student driver does not begin by studying parts of the engine or how internal combustion works or how energy is transmitted to move the car forward or backward. One does not need to know these to become a competent driver. Many writers on management take that approach — here's how you do this or that. Mine is different; it starts with a clinician's view of human nature.

Let me explain. Among characteristics shared by most mammals, organized behavior in reaching an objective is common and typically species specific. Often the objective is to acquire food or provide defense against a threat, but invariably the purpose of such collective behavior is to achieve a specific result. My two careers, first in patient care, research and teaching at the Massachusetts General Hospital, followed by three decades in management as CEO of another Harvard major teaching hospital, Boston's Beth Israel (now Beth Israel Deaconess Medical Center), led me to appreciate that humans, too, share comparable species-specific behavior—acting collectively to achieve a mission. While advances in human mentation and technology create diversity among the immediate ends of this universal characteristic of human behavior, its basic nature is species-specific with a common purpose, like that of other mammals, to achieve a specific objective. This has been true of human nature at least since hunter-gatherers joined collectively to achieve greater success than by acting alone, that is by forming organizations to do work.

To learn the practice of medicine, we begin with human anatomy and physiology. People do differ from one another, as do their illnesses even with identical diagnostic titles, such as pneumonia or cancer. Similarly, individuals' ways of thinking and acting may differ, but their anatomy, physiology, and human nature have not changed over many thousands of years. And while uniqueness among individuals is obvious, there is a fundamental commonality among human beings — the centuries-long way people form organizations to accomplish work. Because of that commonality, it is reasonable to start by exploring whether there may be a common anatomy and physiology of organizations, hoping that if so, and we come to understand that, we can become more thoughtful and effective, not only as a Chief Executive Officer but as manager at any level.

One does not begin the practice of medicine by coming up with imaginative new concepts. While they may follow, we start with human anatomy and physiology, then go on to what appears to be valid through observation, investigation, the result of trial and proof, at times tentatively adding what is not yet proven but seems likely to be so. We revise these as facts and experience accumulates. From these basics, the student — vicariously and passively at first and later through further study and increasing participation in diagnosis and treatment — gains awareness in how to observe, judge, and ultimately act.

Like the practice of medicine, the management of human organizations may best be taught starting with the remarkable common anatomy and physiology of organizations, that is their common structure, work, roles, and internal relationships. Then just as the medical student advances from basic sciences to interact with patients, first as observer and then increasingly involved hands-on to reach independent practice — as you read further, you share my experiences, insights, and lessons learned. These are offered to help you become more insightful, a better manager. You may feel that some of what follows is "old stuff" and ask where is the innovation a new book could offer, yet our basic thesis may be new to many readers, offering useful insight into organizations established to do work and the people who make that so. The book will offer a grounding for managers and would-be managers, not only those of hospitals but thoughtful members of any organization. Faculty and students of organization and management should find it informative, as will physicians, nurses and other hospital personnel. And given the general interest in what goes on in a hospital (and perhaps other organizations), it could attract even wider an audience.

Warmly I thank and credit many others within and well beyond Beth Israel Deaconess Medical Center and Harvard Medical School, especially my forbearing wife, Adrienne, and children, Julia and David, and all who helped educate me in learning, reflecting on, and carrying out my roles in academic medicine and in management. This includes a spate of co-workers, mentors, advisors, and colleagues including Jack Kasten, Edna Homa, David Dolins, Sandra Fenwick, Laura Avakian, Joyce Clifford, Ruth Patterson, J. Antony Swartz-Lloyd, Eugene Wallace, Rodger Daniels, Frank Sullivan, Drs. David Freiman, Howard Hiatt, Howard Frazier, William Silen, Daniel Tosteson, Robert Ebert, Walter Bauer, Lloyd "Holly" Smith, Daniel Federman, each board chair during my tenure as CEO from 1966 to 1996: Samuel Slosberg, Irving Rabb, Sidney Stoneman, Bernard Grossman, Stanley Feldberg, Norman Leventhal, Eliot Snider, Phillip Nexon, Edward Linde, Edward Rudman, Stephen Kay, several thoughtful consultants and many other friends and colleagues, especially my loyal office staff— Susan Lubars, Karen Giffen, Judy Walls and Linda Nexon, along with the authors cited throughout this book.

CHAPTER 1: ORGANIZATIONS

ORGANIZATIONS, WORK AND WORK ROLES
WHAT IS WORK?

Organizations are created to pursue a mission. They do so by performing the work designed to fulfill that mission. Unless the organization is a partnership only of equals with no subordinate positions, the organization will be a hierarchy. It will exist on two or more levels, each subordinate to the one above it. Overseeing it will be the governing body — the owner(s) or a board of directors or trustees acting as owner and legally committed to govern by establishing operating policy, strategy, overseeing finances, and hiring and reviewing the operating manager, who serves as chief executive officer (CEO), and is accountable to the governing body for getting done the work designated to fulfill the organization's mission.

What is meant by "work?" While differing work roles call for differing degrees of *physical effort* — one person digs ditches, one takes photos, and another thinks up a marketing plan, what is common to all work roles is *decision-making*. Each individual has prescribed actions — what to do by when — but each also is required to make judgments in carrying out what he or she must do. Even at entry level, a housekeeping worker must decide when to change the water in the mopping bucket, or report to his or her manager whether or not the new detergent, in the worker's judgment, is satisfactory in getting the job done. Decision-making is the characteristic common to all employment roles. Some decisions are pre-scribed, such as, "When the temperature reaches 120 degrees, turn off the heat." Others are at the worker's discretion, such as using one's judgment on today's projected weather, to paint inside or outside the house. Emphasizing, "... employed people are paid for making decisions, they are not paid for obeying rules," Wilfred Brown[2] concludes, "*Employment Work* is the application of knowledge and the exercise of discretion within limits prescribed by the immediate manager and by higher policies toward an objective set by the immediate manager, the whole being carried out within an employment contract."

Among writers on organization and management, the late Elliott Jaques[3] is, I feel, underappreciated. Educated as a psychoanalyst, he served with considerable success as consultant to The United States Army and businesses world-wide. The lack of familiarity managers and business writers may have with his work might be related to Jaques's challenging writing style, ultimately approached by the addition of diagrams to his texts, intended but failing to clarify. Nevertheless, Jaques's thoughtful ideas provide insight into the nature of the well-functioning organization established to do work.

Jaques defines work as goal-directed behavior, carrying out tasks to produce a given output within a given time, and do so with given method, financial, physical, and organizational resources, and conforming to the organization's policies, regulations, and procedures. A task is an assignment to achieve a given goal ("what-by-when") with allocated resources and methods and within prescribed limits. In organizational hierarchies, tasks are assigned by a person's manager or by another, a supervisor, acting for that manager.

[2] Brown,W. Organization. London: Heinemann Educational Books. 1971
[3] Jaques E. Requisite Organization. Arlington VA: Cason Hall & Co. 1996

In order to accomplish that work, the individual must apply the necessary knowledge with skill, exercising appropriate discretion and judgment in making decisions needed to reach the assigned goal. Agreeing with Wilfred Brown, Jaques considers work as including both good judgment and decision-making, finding one's way through the changing complex of variables that might arise as the task is being carried out. Good judgment and good decision-making depend upon the intrinsic capability of the individual. That capability is made up of his or her relevant skill, intrinsic and acquired, his or her own store of and ability to access available knowledge, and his or her motivation.

ORGANIZATIONS
CLARITY IN DESCRIBING WORK ROLES
Roles in most organizations may differ one from another. Because the job title might not tell what the worker actually does, each role requires further definition, including:

- Duties of the role, both general and specific.
- Time-line for carrying out various duties, that is "what-by-when."
- Degree of discretion the role enjoys.
- Range and limits of authority the role carries.
- To whom that worker is accountable.

Arriving at Beth Israel Hospital in 1966, I had little experience as a manager. My only administrative role had been as chief resident in medicine at the Massachusetts General Hospital, not likely to prime one for leadership of another major research-intensive Boston teaching hospital affiliated with Harvard Medical School. Seeking advice I met with consultant Edna Homa, DBS. (Our initial meeting was memorable. She began, "I don't care what you say, and I don't care what you do, but I do care that you say what you do and you do what you say.")

Dr. Homa directed me to several books; these helped me better understand organization, management, and leadership.

One was "Organization" by Lord Wilfred Brown. He had been chairman of Glasgow's Glacier Metal Co. Ltd. from 1939 to 1965. In Chapter Five, "What is Work?" Lord Brown writes:

> "The following advertisement appeared in a leading Sunday newspaper: Shop Superintendent. Competent and experienced man required to take complete charge of sheet metal and machine shop engaged in commercial work. The aim is expansion particularly in the stainless-steel field and applicants must be up to date in methods..."

He pointed out the ad's faults. "For example, the term 'complete charge of' implies that nobody else in the company has any accountability for the 'sheet metal and machine shop' ... Nobody reading the description can gain any real knowledge of the work involved except through inference." Work of any sort, Lord Brown emphasized, begins with decision-making, i.e., what to do. Every role has both its prescribed elements and its limits of discretion; each worker is mandated and has authority to do certain things but not others. (For example, as CEO, I had authority to recommend to the Hospital's Board the operating budget for next year but only the Board had authority to approve it.) And each task has (or should have) a specified time of completion.

Returning to the original advertisement, Lord Brown offers a rewrite, "The company employs X people in total and produces sheet metal products. It aims to expand the production of those made of stainless steel. It operates one manufacturing department which employs Y people and uses metal-forming and machining processes. A superintendent is required to manage this department. The salary range is £A to £B per year. Please write for a specification of the role and an application form. " (Note that here, "superintendent" implies the individual selected will be a *manager*, a designation differing from the distinction between these two roles I later make.)

Lord Brown's analysis of work made sense, and his comments on want-ads even more so when years later I faced a major recruiting need. The elderly Director of Nursing I met on arrival at BI had been problematic; even I could sense her performance was less than ideal. I was relieved when shortly she retired. Seeking advice from nurse leaders at local hospitals and schools of nursing, I was assured that many excellent candidates would surface, but upon my asking them to suggest such individuals, none came forth with names. I probed several of our own nursing staff for their thoughts — had any come across someone they felt might fill the role of top nursing manager? That uncovered one name per seven nurse-years of experience. The best candidate was Ruth Patterson, heading OR nursing at a suburban community hospital. She seemed straightforward, thoughtful, and lucid, had a good track record and reference evaluations. I was pleased and relieved when she accepted the role of nursing director.

It was an unusual placement for a major teaching hospital. Ms. Patterson had only an RN and no bachelor's or higher degree. Several of the city's nurse leaders — none having offered names of potential candidates — chastised me for the choice. Nonetheless, Ms. Patterson improved both our staffing and nursing performance. I was content with her achievements but did not yet understand how high the standard of nursing could or should rise.

Years later when Ms. Patterson's husband was to transfer to a distant city and she would follow, I knew recruiting would differ from my earlier approach. Returning to Lord Brown's comment on recruitment ads, I placed this in the Journal of Nursing Administration:

> Our Director of Nursing is leaving because her husband
> has been transferred to a distant city. In the five years
> of her tenure at Boston's Beth Israel Hospital, Ruth

Patterson has implemented about fifteen years of progress in nursing care and its administration, and in the post-graduate education that make good nurses even better and gratified in their own work. She has been an excellent clinician and a valued member of top management, and both physicians and administrators listen to her because she is worth listening to. She will tell you she has never worked so hard in her life and that it tears her apart to have to leave.

We have 374 medical, surgical, and obstetrical beds; by 1976 there will be 452. Beth Israel Hospital is a major teaching hospital of Harvard Medical School, with full-time clinical departments, extensive house staff, many students, a relatively sick House in high census, most of the latest in technology, a considerable interest in innovation both in patient care and management, a willingness to relate to the other institutions in the area, a sound capacity for program and budget planning, and the ability to stick to the budget. The Director of Nursing runs a shop of 470 FTE presently, covering all Inpatient Units, Emergency Unit, Outpatient Services, Operating and Recovery Rooms, Labor and Delivery Rooms, several Satellite Clinics, and a strong Staff Education and Development department. If you have got what it takes, you will become a true colleague of the Professors of Medicine, Surgery, Anesthesia, etc., just as our present Director has.

If this sounds right for you and for us, please write to Mitchell T. Rabkin, M.D., General Director, Beth Israel Hospital, 330 Brookline Avenue, Boston, Mass. 02215, giving details of your career and salary history.

At the time, Joyce C. Clifford, RN, BS, MS was on the faculty of the Indiana University School of Nursing but thinking of returning to her native New England and to hospital nursing administration. Aware of her interest, a colleague alerted her to that journal issue and an ad for a nurse leader at a Boston hospital. What she referred to was the ad from another hospital, but Joyce Clifford never got past ours. I am eternally grateful to Lord Brown for emphasizing clarity on the nature of roles and relationships. (More later about Joyce Clifford, her brilliant career with us, and her impact on nursing at BI and world-wide.)

ORGANIZATIONS
ACCOUNTABILITY vs. AUTHORITY

Check out this scenario: A manufacturing unit of thirty people, one of several in a large factory. The VP for production approaches one of its workers.

"Charlie, you've been doing a fine job for the past twelve years. With Tom retiring, I'd like you to be the new manager."

Charlie smiles, "Thanks. That's great. I've been with these 'SoB's for a dozen years, and I know every trick they play. You can bet, with me as manager, they're not going to get away with anything. I'll keep their noses to the grindstone!" OOPS! Up to this moment, Charlie, too, was one of "...these SoB's."

What Charlie sees in being a manager is *authority*. He's determined to exercise his new authority, so nobody "...gets away with anything." Sadly, Charlie (and perhaps his own manager) does not grasp what it means to be a manager. Wilfred Brown offers insight:

- In organizations employing people, there are roles to which more work is allotted than a single occupant of the role personally can perform. Assume that Smith occupies one of these roles.

- Smith must arrange for some of his/her work to be carried out by others.
- While Smith personally does not do all the work allotted to his/her role, he/she is accountable to higher authority for the manner in which all of it is carried out — quality, quantity, timing.
- Smith must be authorized to assess the competence of those proposed and those appointed to do parts of his/her work on his/her behalf, and both to approve and to veto the appointment of persons directly subordinate to him/her to carry out some of this work.
- Smith must be authorized to decide whether or not a subordinate be retained in his/her role. If Smith is ordered to retain a subordinate who is not, in his/her judicious opinion, capable of discharging the work that Smith allocates, then Smith cannot be held accountable for the results that follow. A manager cannot be held accountable for unsatisfactory work performance of a subordinate whom he/she legitimately feels should not be in that work unit; the manager must be able to reject the worker from that employment once objectively found not to perform to the standards set for that role.

What is the authority of a manager? It includes the authority to hire, train, motivate, encourage, commend, correct, counsel, warn and, should performance remain unsatisfactory, deselect an individual from that role to another or from his/her unit. Why does the manager have that authority? It is so the manager can fulfill his or her *accountability* to his or her own manager, to get done all components of the work specified, directly by him or her and by his or her subordinates, and meet its specified quality, quantity, and timing.

By understanding that *accountability is the key characteristic of the managerial role, and authority is secondary by virtue of that accountability,* the manager will appreciate that the role is not to cast a critical eye on the performance of his or her employees and restrain or punish in response but rather to do everything appropriate he or she can to enable her/his employees to carry out fully and as perfectly as possible their role accountability, just as the manager works to fulfill accountability to her/his manager.

Max DePree, former CEO of the Herman Miller Company, widely recognized as a best place to work and one of the best run organizations, wrote, "The first responsibility of a leader is to define reality. The last is to say thank you. In between the two, the leader must become a servant and a debtor."[4] Being the servant of one's subordinates means that you are doing everything for them that you can as manager, whether through information, education, praise, counseling, motivation, support, etc., to get the assigned work done at least as well and as timely as specified and ideally even better. You owe this to those you manage; that is part of your accountability. When this concept is neither understood nor carried out, a manager loses effectiveness.

ORGANIZATIONS
RELATIONSHIPS ARE DEFINED BY ROLES

One way to understand roles in an organization is through the relationship of one individual to another. What comes to mind first might be that of a "boss" and someone to whom he or she gives directions. The general terms are "manager" and "subordinate." It is the successive tiers of managers and subordinates that create the "organizational hierarchy," for example the series of steps in an army from 4-Star General level by level down to Private.

The Manager-Subordinate Relationship

Why the need for "manager?" Someone is given the role of manager because there is more work for which he or she is accountable than he or she can do alone. To fulfill that accountability, the manager is as-

---

[4] DePree M. Leadership Is an Art. East Lansing, MI: Michigan State University Press, 1987.

signed one or more subordinate individuals. They will relate to their manager as described, for example, by Rowbottom et al,[5] referring to work by Wilfred Brown and Elliott Jaques. Let's call the manager "A" and subordinate "B."

- A will prescribe B's work, assign the requisite tasks to B to carry out that work. A is responsible to assure that the needed materials are available and accessible for the work to be completed.
- A will judge the performance of B in that role. A is responsible to tell B the objectives and methods of the assigned tasks as appropriate, and to counsel B (praise, advise how to do better, after learning what limitations B felt he or she encountered that may have hampered ideal performance), all following objective evaluation of B's performance.
- A may initiate the transfer of B from the specific role currently occupied, if A judges B's performance, after appropriate feedback, education, counseling and warning, unable to reach an adequate standard.
- A may determine, within policies set by higher authorities, the rewards of B (bonus, promotion, etc.).
- A may veto the proposed appointment of B to the role of his/her subordinate, if A legitimately feels that B cannot accomplish the requisite tasks.

The Supervisory Relationship

When manager A needs help in managing the work of subordinate B, a supervisor accountable to A can assist A to carry out his or her role. The supervisor cannot override his/her manager's authority but is accountable for supporting the manager's directives, as follows

- Assign work to B.
- Clarify the duties of B.

---

[5] Rowbottom R, et. al. Hospital Organization. London: Heinemann Educational Books, Ltd., 1973.

- Deal with immediate work problems of B and attempt to resolve them.
- Monitor the performance of B, assess it, and report his/her judgment to A.

The supervisor does not have the right to veto the appointment of B or initiate dismissal of B but can recommend judgments to A about B's performance, negative and positive. The supervisor is not accountable for the work performance of B; that remains the accountability of the manager.

At its most circumscribed definition, a Chief Operating Officer (COO) occupies the role of supervisor, but her/his range of authority to resolve work problems of subordinates is greater, for example, than that of a supervisor lower in the organizational hierarchy, such as a supervisor in an organization's laundry or housekeeping. (For example, my Chief Operating Officer had authority to make certain policy decisions, simply alerting me to be aware of his choices and the reasons for these, without my prior approval.)

The Prescribing Relationship

In a clinical or other situation, the prescriber of a task or action may not necessarily be the manager of the individual directed to carry it out. The prescriber is accountable to his/her manager for the action ordered, and the receiver of the prescribed action is accountable to his or her manager for carrying out the action ordered, within limits generally defined and mutually understood. Example: a physician may "order" or prescribe a task to be done by a nurse, or a consultant may recommend a course of treatment to the physician actually taking care of the patient. In such instances, the "ordering" physician and the recipient of the order or recommendation are not necessarily in a manager-subordinate relationship. In this relationship:

- The doctor or other authority prescribes the treatment or other specific services that another individual should or might appropriately do.
- The prescribing person must respond to comments and questions from the recipient about the actions prescribed and events that might follow their administration.
- The individual responding to the authority prescribing a certain action may delegate the needed response to his or her subordinate (a head nurse may direct another of her/his staff to carry out the order) but remains accountable to his/her manager for the proper carrying out of the action prescribed.
- In an instance where, for example, a nurse or physician makes the informed judgment that the action prescribed for them to take would not be appropriate, he or she has the right and responsibility to question the prescribing doctor. If the resulting discussion fails to convince the nurse or physician that the action should be taken as prescribed, she or he can refuse to do so and refer the matter to her or his manager. While rare, should reasoned judgment sustain uncertainty, the matter in question should be escalated to higher authorities.

The Coordinating Relationship

Where several individuals are assembled to carry out a task, and coordination among them is required but manager-subordinate or supervisory relationships alone are not appropriate, a coordinating role may be required. Examples of such instances are the production of a report involving input from several departments, or the implementation of a new multidisciplinary project, or a multidisciplinary response to an emergency, such as an institutional power loss or nearby disaster.

- The coordinator works within the framework of the specific task assigned, negotiating the work to be assigned and carried out, arranging for the resources needed, helping to overcome problems encountered in getting the task done, monitoring, and reporting the progress achieved to the individual who appointed her or him to the role.

- The coordinator has authority to arrange meetings among participants, propose actions, obtain first-hand knowledge of progress, determine who shall do what among the work to accomplish the task.
- The coordinator can attempt to resolve disagreement among the participants but cannot issue overriding instructions if the disagreement is sustained; for resolution the involved participants have direct access to the higher authority who set the task to be accomplished.
- The coordinator may be lower on the organizational hierarchy than some of the participants in the task needing coordination, yet retains the limited but designated authority appropriate to the coordinator role.

The Monitoring Relationship

At times it is necessary to ensure that the activities of an individual or group conform to set standards, and a managerial or supervisory relationship is not called for or needs supplementing. Examples might be monitoring that hallways are clear and not in violation of fire regulations, seeing that designated levels of expenditure are not exceeded, that the technical standard of a projected work is maintained.

The person in a monitoring role is accountable for:

- Obtaining first-hand knowledge of the activities and any problems facing those accountable for the actions being monitored.
- Where indicated, persuading those being monitored to modify their performance in order to achieve the goals set.
- If failing to negotiate improvements with individuals monitored, trying to negotiate same with their managers.
- Reporting progress to the authority to whom he/she is accountable, any significant deviation from the performance standards sought, and the result of efforts to negotiate improvements.

The Service Relationship

While all workers provide one set of services or another, in this relationship the individual seeking service decides what service he or she needs according to the specific occasion. One example is where a surgeon operating on a patient calls for a pathologist to respond in timely fashion to create a "frozen section" microscopic examination and report on a sample of tissue just removed from the operated patient still under anesthesia in order to determine further extent of surgery. Where the service requested is not felt appropriate, the service-giver may consult with the requester to redefine the request. For example, a radiologist asked for a specific x-ray view may discuss with the requester the limitations of his/her request and recommend a different view or procedure. In the service relationship:

- An individual may, at his or her own discretion, request specific services from another individual assigned a service-giving role, within limits defined as to the nature and timing of the service.
- The service-giver is accountable to his or her manager for providing the services requested, within limits of the resources available, and policies on the nature and timing of service to be delivered.
- Should there be any issues unresolved between the individual requesting the service and the individual designated to supply it, or their respective managers, on the nature, timing, priority, or quality of the service requested, there is ultimately a common manager at the cross-over point to resolve the issue.

There is a variant of the service-giving relationship where aspects or timing of specific services can be directed by someone not the manager of the service-giving individual. For example, the housekeeper on a nursing unit has a series of routine and repetitive tasks assigned by his or her manager — doing what by when — but depending on the situation perceived at any time by the nursing staff may be requested to shift to another priority among their designated responsibilities — the housekeeper will shift from cleaning the room of a discharged patient to cleaning up a major spill of food as a cart tumbles coming off the unit's elevator.

Note that none of the roles described above is that of "leader." The designation of leader defines no specific role in an organizational hierarchy; it defines a behavior. At any level, a manager can and should be a leader, but it is not an inevitable part of the management role in practice. A subordinate can become a leader as well, to some extent in pursuing the specific work role she/he has been given or some unrelated effort. If a manager at any level handles well the complexity of her/his tasks, that manager will earn personal authority, but as Elliott Jaques emphasizes, it is not the authority specified in the job description of "manager." Personally and individually earned, leadership authority is given by subordinates and can be recognized by others as well. It is their confidence in the manager's effectiveness to do her/his own work and to lead her/his subordinates to do their work well. Given only by subordinates, that confidence generates a category of authority separate from that defined by the manager's job description.

The manager sets the purpose and direction for one or more subordinates to carry out; the leader gets them to move along with her/him and with each other to do the designated work with competence and full commitment. Without followers there is no leader! Except for situations such as the military, where subordinates must follow directions from above, followers emerge only when the manager personally earns the authority to be seen as a leader.

This definition properly places the concept of "leader." Much seems written about "leadership style," but the fact is that style of performance among managers may vary dramatically and does not determine their effectiveness as manager. To the extent a manager gains committed followers, she or he becomes a leader; otherwise, her/his effectiveness as manager becomes weakened or lost.

ORGANIZATIONS

PROFESSIONALISM IN EVERY WORK ROLE

For every role in an organization, there are (a) tasks *prescribed* and (b) activities that are discretionary. While prescribed tasks are clearly defined, discretionary actions are areas of autonomy related to the particular role. For every role, autonomy has its boundaries, placed by overall institutional policy and the nature of each role. While the employee *satisfactorily* fulfills his or her role in carrying out the tasks specifically prescribed, within its discretionary areas the worker can demonstrate *excellence*.

For example, the hospital photographer is alerted that the President of the United States is scheduled to arrive in the lobby tomorrow at 10 A.M. The photographer's manager directs him/her to be there, set up, and ready to go by 9:30. The manager does not dictate specifically where and when to point and click, only that the shots should include the President with the Board Chair, try to get the hospital's logo in the background, etc. The actual photo shots and camera settings are within the photographer's discretion, the role's area of autonomy. And that is where the photographer will go beyond competence to demonstrate excellence.

Some may argue, "But at entry level, the housekeeper mopping the floor, where is the autonomy?" Discretion is more limited, but it still exists. When does the housekeeper decide to change water in the bucket? Where to place the sign warning passers-by of a wet floor, or when to judge the mop needs replacement, or that the new cleanser may seem more effective but leaves scratches? Autonomous decision-making for the housekeeper, limited as in every organizational role, can mean the difference between excellence and less, yet still fulfilling the role's prescribed elements.

Consider the physician or nurse "professionals" who utilize his or her knowledge, experience, and judgment in the interests of the client, his or her patient. The excellent physician goes beyond the role's prescribed elements to exercise discretionary elements in responding to the patient's needs. (While it might be argued — or should be — that the clinician warms the stethoscope diaphragm on his/her palm before placing it on the patient's bare skin, a discretionary excellence might be gently placing one's other hand on the patient's shoulder while listening to the chest. That connection could lessen the depersonalization of that activity.)

At every organizational level, workers are expected to use their knowledge, experience, and judgment in the interests of the "client." In any organization, the "client" is defined by mission. Understanding that mission, subscribing to it and knowing how one's role applies, we try to go beyond doing simply what is prescribed, through our role's discretionary actions in the interests of the organization's mission. It follows that through their collective discretionary use of experience, knowledge, and skills, all staff and employees together create a common thread of professionalism, forging an unique colleagueship throughout the organization.

Some writers distinguish "operational" from "non-operational" roles, arguing, for example, physician, nurse, transporter, and orderly are operational roles while purchasing, maintenance, and billing are not. That's like arguing the automobile's engine and drive shaft are operating entities, but the seats, air-conditioning, and windows are not. One needs balanced ecology among all roles, or the mission will be hard to accomplish if at all. For an organization to be effective, all roles are operating to achieve the mission and should be so considered. Unfortunately, some look on those at lower levels of the organization as doing menial, unprofessional, less important work than theirs. They may voice appreciation of subordinates as a kindly gesture rather than recognize the linkage among all roles. Awareness of this unique bond of professionalism throughout the organization is to understand the true colleagueship among all workers in the hospital and other organizations.

I savor the illustrative aphorism shared with me by J. Antony Swartz-Lloyd, then our VP for Communications, "The competent amateur makes sure everything goes right; the competent professional makes sure nothing goes wrong."

ORGANIZATIONS
THE PETER PRINCIPLE

In *The Peter Principle: Why Things Always Go Wrong,*[6] authors Laurence J. Peter and Raymond Hull define the "Peter Principle" as being "...promoted to one's level of incompetence." Elliott Jaques relates competence to the complexity of work an individual can handle effectively, arguing that the range of capability of individual performance in a hierarchical organization set up to do work is not represented by a smooth bell curve, such as we see in IQ. It is, he argues, a series of discontinuous steps, each a quantum leap above the prior step. Within each step, there is a bell curve of capability, but as Peter and Hull point out, an individual who performs well within one level of work complexity may fail when promoted up to the next. The level to which an individual can actually rise will depend not on opportunity but upon the intrinsic capability of that individual. Any person's capability becomes fully expressed with maturity and through experience, but according to Jaques, is ultimately limited to one level or another for every individual.

Jaques relates these levels of individual capability to the levels of complexity of work an individual can do. He describes these in terms of "time-span," the maximum period of time a manager will expect and allow his or her subordinate to work without reviewing the results.

Unfortunate about the Peter Principle concept is the term "incompetence," which implies that the individual is somehow incompetent. The fact that one cannot keep a tune or draw accurately carries no such denigration, nor does the situation where a musician is quite capable

---

[6] Peter LJ, Hull R. The Peter Principle. New York, Harper Collins Publishers, Reprinted October 2011.

but unable to perform at the standard required by a major symphony orchestra. In an organizational hierarchy, someone may be surpassingly competent at one level, yet crash when promoted upward to the next level of complexity.

I knew of one academic medical center where a physician of considerable merit was promoted to chair one of its clinical departments. Within months division heads under that physician, chairs of other clinical departments, and administrators agreed the appointee was not performing as required and should not continue in that role.

In academic medical centers, there are two distinct yet interrelated roles for a department chair. The academic role includes the scholarly activities of teaching and supervising clinical medicine and both directing and carrying out research; for these the chair is primarily accountable to the medical school dean. Usually a professorial position entailing academic tenure, it is not often subject to recall for substandard academic management. The second role, administratively managing the department and its activities of patient care, teaching, and research, includes budget responsibilities and working collaboratively with hospital colleagues, clinical and administrative, in carrying out the institution's mission. In that administrative role, the department chair is accountable to the hospital board of trustees through the CEO and/or the dean if the hospital is owned by the medical school. The administrative role usually carries no tenure guarantee. In this instance, it became possible for the hospital CEO, once reasonably certain of inadequacy in the administrative role through discussions over time with the chairman under consideration, and later with immediate subordinates, chairs of other services, several administrators, and the board of trustees and dean, to determine that this individual must step down as department chair.

Here was a person already accomplishing much over a distinguished career, enjoying a well-deserved reputation as expert clinician, outstanding research scientist, lucid teacher and mentor. Sadly, many conversations had led to no improvement in administrative management of the department. It was not comfortable for the CEO to oblige this outstanding academician to step down as chair and return to direct the subspecialty division previously headed, a role that had led to wide respect. Tense and awkward, the administrative action had become imperative, otherwise the department would have suffered a spate of departures.

One mistake an executive can make in dealing with a manager not meeting performance standards is to appoint a "co-leader," someone to "help" the failing individual manage. While it may appear face-saving, is it less embarrassing to be told one needs, in essence, a baby-sitter than it is to be deposed? And it never works.

In this instance, the Peter Principle was validated. The following day on entering the hospital, now one step down in the organization and managing the division formerly chaired, this individual seemed to appear ten years younger. Not happy in the former role but out of loyalty to department and hospital, the former chairman had kept at it, doing one's best. It had been, as Peter and Hull so harshly put it, a promotion to one's level of incompetence. Back heading the subspecialty division, this academician resumed the brilliant performance of earlier years and furthered a sterling reputation of excellent clinician, teacher, and research scholar. From someone provoking deep concerns shared by many colleagues, here was an outstanding individual who once more became a star of whom most became truly fond and all were proud.

Despite the embarrassment of being moved down a step in the organizational hierarchy, it was a classic instance of moving from a level of complexity one could not master to one fulfilled through excellent performance. The move was as much kindness to the physician as it was to the institution. And the individual's grace in accepting the change added further luster to the stature of this exceptional academician.

CHAPTER 2: HOSPITAL (AND OTHER) BOARDS

INTRODUCTION

In a crisp description of the board's role in governance of the nonprofit hospital, Lesley Rosenthal, general counsel, Lincoln Center for the Performing Arts, and Bart Friedman, senior partner, Cahill Gordon and Reindel LLP, wrote, [7] The board of a well-governed nonprofit organization, like the board of a well-governed profit-making organization, will do all of the following:

- Formulate key corporate policies and strategic goals, focusing both on near-term and longer-term challenges and opportunities.
- Authorize major transactions or other actions.
- Oversee matters critical to the health of the organization — not decisions or approvals about (most) specific matters, which is management's role — but instead those involving fundamental matters such as the viability of its business model, the integrity of its internal systems and controls, and the accuracy of its fi-

---

[7] Rosenthal L, Friedman B. Nonprofit Corporate Governance: The Board's Role. https://corpgov.law.harvard.edu/2012/04/15/nonprofit-corporate-governance-the-boards-role#more-27827 Accessed May 2020.

nancial statements.

- Evaluate and help manage risk.
- Steward the resources of the organization for the longer run, not just by carefully reviewing annual budgets and evaluating operations but also by encouraging foresight through several budget cycles, considering investments in light of future evolution, and planning for future capital needs.
- Mentor senior management, provide resources, advice, and introductions to help facilitate operations.

They add, "In a well-governed organization of either the for-profit or non-profit kind, the board does not permit executives to run and dominate board meetings, set agendas, or determine what information will be provided to board members. Under the leadership of an active and functioning board chair, there is adequate opportunity at board meetings for members to receive and discuss reports not only from the chief executive, but also, as appropriate, directly from other (operating) executives, in-house and outside professionals, and independent consultants if necessary. Time should be reserved for executive sessions, at which management should be excluded, so that its performance may be fully and freely discussed."

The board — at least its major decision-makers — are (or should be) intelligent women and men sincerely involved and committed to govern a positive course for the hospital. They are successful through knowledge, experience, and insight in their respective fields, but they need to understand that the work of for-profit and other volunteer organizations on which they may also serve differs greatly from that of the hospital. Goods and services must be provided whether or not the customer (the patient) can pay and payment rates are often decided by government or private insurers. Where certain indices are deemed by payers such as government to indicate unsatisfactory quality of care, improper billing, or other violations, payment penalties can surface. At academic hospitals, grant money almost never pays the full costs of research supported, and teaching rarely generates revenue. The primary mission of the hospital — patient care — competing with the medical school's primary mission — teaching and research — can create conflict in the allocation of attention and resources, even when both hospital and school exist under unified top management.

A primary task of the hospital CEO is to educate board leadership on the unique nature of the hospital to help board members apply their knowledge toward effective governance. Educating the board goes well beyond orientation sessions and the occasional "retreat." It calls for ongoing openness by the CEO to clarify the complex issues faced, not when the CEO is about to act but earlier, even as an issue might alert the CEO, given its significance and its relevance to the Board's responsibilities or to the perspective and wisdom the board can offer. Beyond setting strategy and policy, the Board is there to "monitor, guide, and enable good management; they do not do it themselves," as Lesley Rosenthal stated in the document quoted above. There should be few restrictions on Board awareness of the CEO's thoughts on major administrative insights and actions.

Candor does not mean the CEO is seeking permission to act. The purpose of candor is to help board leadership (and ultimately the entire board) understand issues facing the hospital and CEO, and over time, the evolution of his/her thinking on decisions and actions made or to be made. Over the course of such transparency, board leadership can offer useful thoughts; some helpful, perhaps others less so, but both board and CEO can gain insight and perspective through candid and collegial discussion.

I met with the board chair at breakfast twice a month, airing the nature and progress of present and anticipated issues of current or potential significance. In some alternate weeks, the vice-chairs joined us on much the same material. All felt free to ask questions and offer comments that often would clarify my thinking, voicing thoughts over time increasingly made relevant through their growing understanding of the unique nature of the hospital. One or more clinical department chiefs often joined these sessions as did one or more administrative vice-presidents. Subjects discussed benefited from their contributions, and they found useful insights offered by board members. Even with this openness, operating decisions remained those of management.

While addition of physicians as voting members of the governing board came slowly at BI, their presence at board meetings (often but not always chiefs of services, the vice president for nursing, and also other administrative vice-presidents) was common. Because many staffed board committees, they could back up committee chairs presenting at meetings. Equally important I wanted them to hear what I reported and to learn directly the reactions and questions board members raised. Since I rarely had all the answers as board members might drill down, the presence of administrative and clinical leaders was invaluable in clarifying, enriching, and occasionally correcting my answers to questions from board members. And I wanted them to know that fair credit was given for their achievements, not co-opted by me.

HOSPITAL (AND OTHER) BOARDS
VARIETIES OF INPUT

Board members learn about the hospital in many ways—through information from the CEO and other managers, by participating in board and committee meetings, from patient care experiences they may have or observe, and from others in conversation. The awareness, vision, interest, and agenda of any may vary. To broaden further our trustees' understanding of the hospital's complexities, we set up quarterly dinner meetings outside the hospital. A private room at the Harvard Club of Boston offered no distraction from restaurant music, television, or crowd noise.

After a brief cocktail hour, guests assembled at five tables, each seating eight to include a mix of physicians, nurses, social workers, administrative staff, and two board members. Once seated all introduced themselves and described their roles. I noted the materials supplied — pens, paper, and the topic for discussion identical for all tables — on which the groups were to focus no later than the appearance of dessert. Each would identify a rapporteur to present a capsule of their respective discussion.

For the topics assigned, there were neither "wrong" responses nor "correct" answers. With the variety of hospital staff at the tables and the perspectives of the trustees, various issues initially arose; some comments were informed, others less so but occasionally passionate. What was said would be kept private; thoughts offered would remain with me for consideration and possible action. Discussions would illuminate, I hoped, issues of which board members might not have been aware. They would glimpse conflicting pressures on the hospital, whether economic, space allocation, academic responsibilities vying with those of patient care, etc. They might hear that teaching generates little or no revenue, and research almost never fully pays for itself, yet these missions are inherent parts of what we do. Other complexities might arise through differing viewpoints on our relationships with Harvard Medical School or other hospitals.

Some topics from our dinner meetings:

- What would make patient care more personalized?
- Given the cost of care, would it make sense to run 24/7 every service at the hospital?
- When a female resident becomes pregnant, she will ultimately lose time in her training around her delivery. How should we deal fairly with (a) the completion of her training, given external accreditation requirements for time spent in actual training? And (b) how do we arrange the needed coverage during her time away?
- When a surgeon states he or she will do the operation, to what extent should a resident participate? What should the patient know?
- As the NIH research budget faces growing demands, some ex-

cellent research scientists late in their research careers but still productive may no longer receive renewed external research funding. What is the responsibility of the hospital and/or medical school in such situations?

These relaxed meetings met with enthusiasm from board members, many feeling their nuanced understanding of the hospital's complexity had been enriched, while enjoying meeting a variety of hospital staff in an informal setting; staff, in turn, savored the opportunity to voice directly with board members their own opinions, insights, and concerns.

HOSPITAL (AND OTHER) BOARDS
A USEFUL IDEA: THE LEADERSHIP LETTER

Among board duties previously noted, Rosenthal and Friedman wrote, "Oversee matters critical to the health of the organization — not decisions or approvals about specific matters, which is management's role — but instead those involving fundamental matters, such as the viability of its business model, the integrity of its internal systems and controls, and the accuracy of its financial statements."

The board is not involved in actual operations, but it is not unreasonable that the board keep aware of efficient functioning of the organization it governs. That is done in part by overview of financial operations, through scrutiny of monthly financial reports, and review of the external auditor's annual audit with its accompanying management letter. Not designed as a performance review of the Chief Financial Officer, the management letter offers (or should offer) experienced oversight of financial operations followed with recommendations for specific improvements. In response the board expects the CFO to list actions proposed or already taken, and it will monitor their accomplishment.

There is no comparably granular review of administrative operations and institutional culture, yet these forge the efficiency and smoothness of organizational functioning. A hospital board may be reassured by a positive bottom line, burgeoning admissions and reports from friends of their satisfaction as patients, but those are results. They are backward-looking and do not illuminate the processes that produced them, or the efficiency and effectiveness with which such processes are carried out. Thus, a board might feel content about operations yet unaware of confused lines of authority or accountability, high turnover, grumbling employees whose ideas and grievances are ignored, ethically questionable management activities, etc. I recall hearing Peter Drucker mention his visit to one organization where several workers were presented to him, being celebrated for an innovation that had made a leap in the efficiency and profit of a particular process. He inquired of the workers when they actually had proposed that advance. The response was something like this, "Every year for the last ten years, but the SoB's didn't listen to us for nine years." Overseeing and managing administrative operations appropriately are delegated to the CEO, but that does not excuse the governing body from awareness of existence and quality of those operations. Periodic external review of "... the integrity of (the hospital's) internal systems and controls" offers that awareness.

The Chief Executive Officer may argue that review of operations is his/her responsibility, is competent to carry out oversight, and can do so without need for impartial external inquiry. Were a Chief Financial Officer to argue the capacity to maintain optimally the financial side of the operation without external review and advice, no board would tolerate his/her refusal to accept and respond to the external auditor's management letter. A CEO might also argue there are consultants already recruited who offer sufficient inquiry. But consultants typically do not offer review of leadership and its impact considered here. They may help in strategic planning, deal with a specific issue in management for which the CEO or board want advice, offer recommendations for cost-cutting, etc. Some CEOs may take advantage of an external expert to serve as confidential mentor and reactor. I have had the benefit of such a relationship with one or another consultant from time to time. None of these helpful arrangements meets the requirements of review envisioned here.

There are accessible indicators of the workplace environment of which a board should be aware, such as clarity of roles and relationships, transparency of management decision-making processes, fair treatment of employees, grievance procedures, turnover, nature and extent of exit interviews, alignment of operating metrics with strategy, leadership style and effectiveness, etc. A colleague and experienced business consultant, Susan Y. Friedman, MBA, and I recently published a proposal for such a review.[8] We labeled the inquiry, "Leadership Letter," comparable to the external auditor's "Management Letter." From our own experience, we have seen organizations in which operational issues had led to dysfunction impairing quality and performance, yet the boards were unaware the organizations they governed should and could have functioned more effectively. At both non-profit and for-profit organizations, the public has seen instances where critical issues went beyond inefficiency, beyond a restive work force, beyond loss of market share, even to violations of the trust an organization assured its customers. This challenge and opportunity to benefit through serious use of a Leadership Letter confront not only boards of hospitals but governing bodies of virtually all organizations, non-profit and for-profit.

---

[8] Friedman SY, Rabkin MT. Where Hospital Boards Often Fail: Auditing Leadership Performance. Acad Med. 2018;93:1613-1626.

CHAPTER 3: IT'S PEOPLE, NOT PRINTOUTS

INTRODUCTION

We've presented the nature of work in an organization and the roles and relationships forging its productive activity. But organization charts and role definitions are not enough. People are not bees in a beehive, genetically programmed to perform specifically designated roles and carry out assigned relationships. Because organizations need other than drone-like behavior, we must enable workers at every level to make decisions enabling them to do their work with excellence in response to all of its challenges.

A comment by business consultant and author Dale Dauten [9] reflects the thoughts of B. Joseph White, then Dean of the Stephen M. Ross School of Business, University of Michigan. White wrote, "My job description, as I saw it, was simple: I would help members of the school community make their individual dreams come true in exchange for their helping make our collective dream for the school come true." Dauten concludes, "The percentage of people who are willing to work very hard to make you successful is far smaller than the percentage of people willing to work very hard to make themselves successful in a way that helps the organization. Pick a team."

---

[9] Dauten D. Leaders help themselves by helping others. Boston Sunday Globe. Boston Works, G3; Dec. 31, 2006.

If "Pick a team" means only the leader's immediate subordinates, I would argue to range broadly and forge knowledgeable, committed people at all levels of the organization. In this and subsequent chapters, I share some of the ways at the hospital we tried to do so.

IT'S PEOPLE, NOT PRINTOUTS
EVERY ROLE IS CRITICAL TO THE MISSION

At his retirement party celebrating thirty-two years of service, Director of Admissions Michael Littmann noted, with turnover and organization changes, he had been accountable to a total of fourteen different vice presidents. Early on he had tried to explain to each what the hospital admitting office confronted and did, and the complexity of his operations. Ultimately, he found it better to invite his new manager to sit with him, learning through actual participation in the hour-by-hour work of admitting and transferring hospital patients.

Employees may know the complexity of their own roles but some, never having experienced work as a nurse or in an admitting office, human resources department, corporate communications office, cafeteria, or laundry, may view other roles as simpler or less consequential. A vivid example, "On Breaking One's Neck," appeared in a 2014 issue of the New York Review of Books[10]. The author had headed medicine at a prestigious academic health center and later was editor of a prominent medical journal. Retired, he remained a respected writer on health care and its reform.

Recounting his recent life-threatening accident and hospitalization, he wrote, "I had never before understood how much good nursing care contributes to patients' safety and comfort, especially when they are very sick or disabled." How had he previously missed that insight?

The medical student newly at the hospital with stethoscope and white coat suffers a limited view compared with one who, before that exciting arrival as student doctor, has volunteered or worked there in a

[10] Relman A. On Breaking One's Neck. New York, NY. The New York Review of Books, February 6, 2014.

non-MD role. Likely he or she has glimpsed already some of the complexity of work of others and the good will and motivation of many making up the hospital work force.

For several years, I headed a month-long course titled, "The Role of the Non-MD in the Hospital." First year Harvard Medical students spent several days each with various hospital workers — nurses, social workers, housekeepers, cafeteria staff. The students wore the appropriate uniforms, were there such for the role, tagging along with a worker in each occupation on their routine of that day serving as mentor. Observing their work, the students garnered how their mentors viewed their roles. Participating to the extent possible, the students — usually assumed to be a worker similar to their mentor — experienced interactions with others throughout the day. Some passersby shared respect, even appreciation; a few conveyed depersonalization, even denigration. The students came to appreciate both the task and human aspects of roles they had never contemplated.

One, previously having earned a PhD in synthetic organic chemistry before medical school, commented, "I thought it was easy to wash walls but never considered whether to start at the top or the bottom or how to do it. I found out the hard part is getting the walls clean."

Such experiential learning takes time, and other things to learn take precedence in medical school. Many don't need such a course; their sensitivity and appreciation tend to stick throughout life. The challenge for CEO and managers is to assure that employees and staff at every level understand and respect the work of each role throughout the hospital and appreciate the collegueship of all that emerges out of understanding and committing to the hospital's mission.

IT'S PEOPLE, NOT PRINTOUTS
EVERY DEPARTMENT IS CRITICAL TO THE MISSION

Any manager makes a mistake should he/she view departments such as Human Resources, Public Affairs, or Development, as less critical, merely carrying out routine functions rather than serving as essential contributors to the institution. To distance these departments encourages mediocrity, denigrates professionalism, and muddies others' appreciation of their worth. Public Affairs becomes viewed as a word merchant, HR as little more than processing employees through uninspired protocols of hiring, training, and exiting. The intelligence, creativity, and motivation of such department heads and their staffs become sandpapered, seemingly validating the uninformed judgment of those who actually foster that mediocrity.

In the eyes of some unenlightened hospital executives and physicians, the same can hold for nursing, but viewing nurses as merely supporting the work of physicians is a grave error. To think of nursing only as "...giving medications, changing bed linens, moving immobile patients from side to side, giving bed baths, taking vital signs, etc.," is tantamount to saying that physicians only "... take medical histories, perform physical exams, write orders, carry out procedures, etc." Perceiving tasks at that superficial level, the uninformed view ignores the full responsibilities and capabilities of nursing or medicine. These are professionals who exercise independent judgment based on extensive knowledge and experience, assign relevance to what they encounter, and take meaningful action in the interest of their patients and the hospital's mission. When viewed merely as performers of routine tasks, denigrated nurses become disenchanted. And today, as physicians find their judgments co-opted by bureaucratic regulations, they, too, can become dispirited, as they struggle to do the professional work for which they are educated and trained.

Managers and employees at every level must understand and respect the purposes and capabilities assigned to all roles within the organization and support enabling those in each to achieve their intrinsic potential.

IT'S PEOPLE, NOT PRINTOUTS
A TELLING OBSERVATION

An observation made by my wife one evening registered deeply with me. A social worker then working at a psychiatric hospital, Adrienne mentioned a psychiatrist she admired for behavior not common in her experience. When they happened both to be in the hospital's coffee shop, she noted his "body English" seemed identical whether he was chatting with a psychiatrist or other professional colleague, a patient or family member, or any hospital employee. Observed from a few tables distant, he seemed no different in manner whatever the role or stature of the individual with whom he was speaking. It was impressive, the equality with which he seemed to approach each contact.

Everyone has his or her own human story, but we are little aware of these for most employees with whom we work. Beyond what we might casually discern, we can miss revealing insights. Working in my office on quiet Saturdays, I'd usually head to the cafeteria at lunchtime. Looking around I tended to join someone familiar sitting alone. This time it was a housekeeper whom I knew only through daily saying hello as I passed him cleaning the corridor outside my office.

After asking if I might join him, I sat down and we began chatting. A bit later, I questioned, "How long have you been working here?"

"Twenty-seven years," was his reply.

"That's quite a long time," I offered.

"Not so long," he said. "I've been working at Children's (Boston Children's Hospital, across the street) twenty-nine years. I work here from seven to three, then run over to Children's from three-thirty to eleven-thirty." Pretty impressive, I thought.

More was to come. Asking about his family, I learned of nine children. Each was a college graduate, several had advanced degrees, and two were academicians at prestigious universities. My casual corridor view had been that of a quiet African-American housekeeper pushing a broom, but the reality was worlds beyond.

At my start as CEO, I wondered why so few African-American, Haitian, and other minority employees seemed poorly responsive to my smiles as we passed in the hospital corridors. A colleague suggested they may have been unsure of how to respond or whether their response would be welcomed. He suggested I speak directly to them, being sure to use their name. (Thanks for ID badges!) The change in my greeting made the difference, usually opening a relationship seeming welcome to both. Remembering names and reaching out extends to encounters anywhere. Head to a cocktail party where you know almost no one and keep mum, then compare that to another where you voice both the name of and interest in one contact after another. "Working the room" with sincerity has its benefits wherever you are.

The richness, joys, and tragedies of individual lives are one basis for our common humanity and mutual respect, strengthening the colleagueship shared among people at all levels of employment.

IT'S PEOPLE, NOT PRINTOUTS
TEAMWORK

Shortly after we acquired our first CT scanner, it seemed that the interval was overly long from one patient leaving the procedure room until the next was scanned. Delay meant minutes mounting to several hours daily when this device was idle in generating diagnostic information and revenue. Was that inevitable or lack of system efficiency? After discussion among relevant managers, we gathered representatives working the four roles influencing those intervals — the secretary in radiology who phones the nursing unit for the patient, the responding nurse who gets the patient ready to go to X-ray, the transporter who delivers the patient there, and the CT technician who handles the patient once arrived.

The initial gathering was fascinating. Each occupational group migrated to a different corner of the meeting room with no interaction from one to another. We began with the question, "Was there unneeded delay in the turnover of CT patients?" Each group proposed one or more of the others as source of any problem, if indeed any remediable delay existed. Most ventured that the interval could be no greater than a few minutes. Their responses led nowhere.

We continued, "Do we really know whether there is a problem of delays?" To get the answer, we needed facts, so would they help us gather the data? We proposed charting the data in a histogram, a vertical bar graph showing the number of instances of time between the call for patient departure from bed to readiness in radiology for scan, using categories of five-minute intervals: one to five, six to ten, eleven to fifteen minutes, etc. That seemed reasonable and all committed to cooperate.

Two weeks later, they were astonished to find the peak number of delays was at the twenty-six to thirty minute interval. They had gathered the data and now, reacting to it collectively, each group seemed more comfortable moving closer toward each other from their respective corners of the room. A more collegial discussion began to emerge week by week. We asked each to describe their involvement in the process — what each does specifically in getting the patient to X-ray and set for their scan. Once shared, the comments of each revealed disparate definitions, such as how quickly the patient should be made ready, guessing when the transporter might arrive; or how rapidly the transporter should come up to the nursing unit for the patient, guessing the time it might take for the nurse to ready the patient. The CT technician mentioned some patients arriving with a running intravenous infusion where their IV pole was too tall to admit entry into the CT room. That required additional time to disassemble. Item after item was discussed, resolutions were proposed, considered, and many adopted.

As insights emerged and changes were made week by week and charting continued, the peak timing intervals gradually shifted to the left, ultimately to the six to ten-minute interval. Initially insular, the four groups merged into a single team of mutually supportive colleagues, collectively celebrating their documented performance improvement. It was impressive — inclusion of the workers involved led to their realization and then acceptance of a problem, its meaningful analysis, and ultimate resolution. This was a process dramatically altering interaction among the participants. Becoming collegial through a blameless process engaging those involved to identify collectively the problem, they joined in the effort and gratification of resolving it. We celebrated this as an example of participative management (see "PREPARE 21") where employees enjoy "the opportunity and responsibility to influence, to the extent of their capabilities."

IT'S PEOPLE, NOT PRINTOUTS
HAPPENSTANCE EVENTS

Happenstance events can both reflect the character of an organization and strengthen it. Some years ago, a young nurse at BI had finished her shift in late afternoon. Returning home and tired from the day's work, she fell asleep, awakening to confront two intruders who had entered to rob the apartment. One told the other that since she had seen them, they must kill her, and he stabbed her several times. The men fled with a TV set, watch, and other items as she called 911. An ICU nurse, she knew the likely anatomy of the wound and anticipated the consequences. The knife had gone into her abdominal aorta, the large artery running from heart to pelvis. Upon very timely arrival of police, she had lost most of her blood volume and was dead.

I was dining at a friend's home that evening and shortly got a call about this horror. Immediately on the phone to Joyce Clifford, vice president for nursing, I found she was already at the nursing unit our victim had just left, breaking the news to its staff. It was a shock for the nurses and then the entire hospital. Many knew and admired the victim. We all felt violated.

In such situations, a "stiff upper lip" might prevail but it is better to deal directly with the issue. It was important that Mrs. Clifford had done so and without delay, breaking the news and helping her colleagues and others to begin working through the inevitable grief. The event and its hospital-wide response pulled the BI family closer together. Perhaps a similar reaction, "Boston Strong," emerged out of the 2013 Boston Marathon bombing, a community-wide feeling of violation triggered by the immediate detailed media sharing of that disaster.

A similar approach applied several years later when a young physician, effective as a clinician but personally troubled from time to time, committed suicide despite alert attention from both psychiatry and a group of concerned peers and mentors. Reaching his chief to foster a repeat of the timely approach Joyce Clifford had taken, I was reassured that he had gone immediately to the victim's peers, then colleagues and family.

There was an extraordinary sequel to our nurse's death. The sense of shock went beyond the hospital, permeating the city. The murder took place on a Saturday afternoon. Later that evening and on Sunday, I reached our trustees to approve a reward for information leading to the arrest and conviction of the killer. On the following morning, I spoke with Boston's Police Chief who called a press conference that afternoon. He detailed efforts his department had underway to find the killer, and I announced a $10,000 reward, then an impressive sum, broadcast on radio and television that evening.

Hours later, early Tuesday morning, the police got a tip. They found the suspect at his home along with the stolen goods, confirming his involvement. The Tuesday morning newspapers and TV broadcasts proclaimed the killer had been found and was in custody. The city's unease was relieved and widely emerged a sense that Beth Israel Hospital and the Boston police had responded well and timely.

Happenstance events in two other employee deaths also brought together hospital staff. Both men were well-liked, competent in their roles, talented, outgoing, and warm. One seemed poorly appreciated by his family, among whom many were professionals in careers better, they seemed to feel, than the profession he had chosen, even though he was an expert in a demanding role. He was also a splendid craftsman, an artisan with excellence of taste, eye, and hand. Many family members came to our remembrance gathering. At the reception following, we displayed many objects he had fashioned, from children's toys to finely crafted jewelry. That display and the feelings voiced by many staff members seemed to hint that while we were celebrating our colleague-ship, the family was — at last and too late — gaining respect for him as an individual, perhaps even realizing that its absence had deprived them of something exquisitely meaningful.

The other instance was that of a talented manager whose family had extruded him upon learning he was gay. Beyond heading his department excellently, he had instilled pride in his workers' performance and in themselves as individuals. Interested in theater, he brought together many employees in out-of-hours productions of musicals and plays. At his remembrance, the massive outpouring of employees and their feelings expressed seemed to open the eyes of his family to what they had missed. For us within the hospital, both tributes strengthened feelings of togetherness; it was a humanistic institution, not only good for patients but for employees as well.

Other happenstance events can have even wider an impact. Highly regarded by colleagues, a young man had begun years before as an orderly. Continuing his education, he advanced to nurse's aide, licensed practical nurse, and finally registered nurse. Appearing at our employee health service with a skin problem, he was diagnosed with Kaposi's sarcoma, suggestive of and then confirmed as HIV infection. He raised the question of being allowed to continue to work, which called for careful consideration. The likelihood of transmission of infection to patients or staff was virtually zero. Intelligent, responsible, and otherwise well, he wanted to work as long as possible, but only if the nurses on his floor would welcome him. They did, we concurred and he continued, performing excellently as before. Treatment at that time was ineffective. Within months his condition deteriorated, he was hospitalized and died.

Several weeks passed, and a local paper of the gay community edi-torialized, commending Beth Israel Hospital on the way we had han-dled his situation. How they had gotten the information was unknown since we had kept it private, but the news sheet knew and published his name. Before long Richard Knox, a top-notch health care reporter then at the Boston Globe, contacted me. Since the story was out, I confirmed its essence, noting this was early in the AIDS epidemic. Attitudes were still forming because of little public understanding of the nature of the infection, its transmissibility, and public health aspects. I emphasized how Knox would approach his write-up could be normative in shaping attitudes of his readership and beyond. If he explained how the hospital had made an informed and thoughtful choice, retaining prime concern for patients with whom that nurse would come in contact, with second-ary concern following for the employees with whom he worked and then for himself, public attitudes thus informed might move in one di-rection. But if Knox implied the hospital was delivering to patients a harbinger of death — even though not so — his report would wrongly alarm the public, hampering their understanding of HIV infection, how caregivers properly deal with it, and the human tragedies it was cre-ating. Richard Knox chose the factual approach. I think his article was critical in forging a rational outlook locally and well beyond.

Another happenstance event seeming to influence public opinion took place early in the conflict in Vietnam. Medical students at Harvard were organizing a protest and asked me to join them in a rally on the nearby medical school quadrangle. Its purpose, they voiced, was to re-cruit public opinion against the war. If so, I suggested, might it be better were we to wear white coats and station participants carrying large pro-test signs at downtown street corners, having alerted the media? A triad of medical student and faculty members — a basic scientist and a prac-ticing clinician — at each location would offer the media something vi-sual for TV and the papers. The resulting demonstration led to wide coverage, locally and beyond, even in Life Magazine. Soon after, it trig-

gered a display by students at Harvard Law School, and others followed. One can speculate on the extent to which New England's attitudes toward the Vietnam War were influenced by these early events,
but had our students remained on the medical school quadrangle, their
protest would have been inconsequential.

Happenstance events can have favorable outcomes, even turn a potential loss into a triumph. In this instance, benefit went to both hospital
and protagonist. One of our best senior managers voiced concern to me
over the upcoming delivery of her second child. Living with her and her
husband, her mother-in-law had been caring capably for their first-born,
but with a newborn soon to arrive, she felt the current arrangement would
not suffice. She was mulling over resigning to stay at home, and with her
mother-in-law's continuing help, care for the two children. But she was
torn, loving her role at BI where she was effective, well-liked, and admired
as a splendid role model of the contemporary working woman.

At the time she voiced her dilemma, the hospital was starting to
plan a new building for outpatient care. My thinking about architecture
of buildings, especially hospital structures, recalls the tale of the president of a college about to re-landscape its commons. Asked where he
wanted the gravel pathways to be placed, he responded not to make any
pathways but wait to see after a year or two where the grass had been
worn down. That would mark the walkways to fill in with stone. For
hospitals, sound physical planning starts neither with vision of a grand
or innovative structure nor the landscape approach that things will find
their most efficient ways: it is through understanding the necessary and
most efficient pathways that people, things, and information should
take. To do that, we needed someone who knew our day-to-day functioning and our goals, who would understand the pathways taken today,
and in concert with every level of projected user of the new building,
project where current and any new pathways could be improved in
order to set understandings and design cooperatively with the architects. I've visited new hospital buildings where those considerations

seem not to have been taken, only to fossilize inefficiency, lose warmth, and add inconvenience to users.

As I mulled over the need for someone in that role, it was happenstance that this executive presented her dilemma to me. Already she had a sound grasp of the activities to take place in the existing and projected buildings and how the two would relate to each other. She had the skills to work with physicians, nurses, transporters, housekeepers, maintenance, etc., and that critical component of users, the patient, to elicit a wide range of ideas for the new building. She would do well putting them together for the hospital executive team, engage effectively with the architects, and later elicit critiques from even wider a group of hospital staff, potential users, and onlookers as drawings, architectural models, and simulated full-sized spaces would surface. Time consuming, such queries are essential. The architects cannot know the multitude of specific activities taking place in a hospital, nor can they project alone what new efforts may demand. Like the aphorism, "Measure twice before you cut," architects need to know details of the activities they will enclose. I know of a hospital in another city where a new office for a department chair was built without his input of the activities to take place within. It accommodated the physician and three visitors. Problem: each morning he met daily with ten residents in the office and could not accept the new place. The structure was then enlarged, reworked with his input, but even more telling an issue turned emerged: hospital management's expectation that the doctor personally was responsible for the added cost. Their argument, "You ordered the renovation." That led to his move to another institution.

When I asked my colleague to meet with me, she may have been thinking I might solicit her thoughts on the *bon voyage* party she surely deserved. Instead, I proposed a half-time position acting as liaison between the anticipated users of the new building and the architects, so that neither would fail to understand the issues and responses of the other in order to reach consensus.

And there was more in the package proposed. While the position was half-time and the salary similarly halved, she was to determine when her need at home was such that she could commit sixty percent time at the hospital, later seventy percent, etc., at her own judgment. And I guaranteed that this change to half-time and eventually to full-time would impair neither her progress in salary nor in her potential for rising along the executive ladder. Months later, after she had progressed to the ninety percent level, I pressed to resume salary at 100 percent of where it should be, knowing she devoted far more effort than called for during any of the truncated times from fifty percent on. She declined, arguing that at the ninety percent level, she need not feel guilty about the occasional need to meet with her children's teachers or take them to a medical appointment. Agreeing, I upped her salary anyway since she had been delivering value well over 100 percent from the start.

The arrangement worked out beautifully. About to complete its third decade, the "new" building, on the corner of Longwood and Brookline Avenues, still works efficiently. It continues to feel fresh, convenient, easy to navigate, and friendly. And not long after I left BI as CEO, this highly competent woman was recruited to become Chief Operating Officer at a hospital nationally ranking number one in its category, where she excelled, and over the past seven years continues there with sterling performance as its Chief Executive Officer.

CHAPTER 4: BEING CEO

DECISION-MAKING

The chief executive officer has primary accountability for and authority to make the organization's major operating decisions. Most survey staff and others for data and opinions on which to base action; few act alone. It's never wise to ignore those likely to be affected or to have relevant data or insights; to do so may suggest their inputs are not valuable or imply that the decision's consequences will have negligible impact on their work or accountability.

A reporter once described my decision-making as "management by consensus." I disagree. With management by consensus, decision-making awaits consensus by those brought together to consider the issue. That can lead to problematic choices and muddy accountability. Gathering information and opinion to weigh consequences differs from seeking consensus. Management issues can be complex; perspectives and opinions can vary among individuals, none of which alone may offer full understanding of the issue, its genesis or consequences to follow. A better decision is likely to emerge through considering views among both those who may be most knowledgeable and those likely to be affected. The CEO must assign relevance to the spectrum of views — some informants are more perceptive, others, less objective. A few might allow personal issues to override institutional needs. Questioning a considered range of people is not management by consensus; it is a process to improve understanding of complex issues and more reasoned decisions.

To be inclusive doesn't mean the CEO must secure unanimity but emphasizes he/she values broad input and discussion, and that others most involved be as well informed as possible.

Wrongly attributed to Donald Rumsfeld, former Secretary of Defense,[11] is the statement, "There are known knowns. These are things we know that we know. There are known unknowns. That is to say, there are things that we know we don't know. But there are also unknown unknowns. These are things we don't know we don't know." These could be relevant knowns but unexplored should the decision-maker fail to counsel with others, or as we note later, unexplored with himself or herself.

To the extent one works with others exploring causation, options, and consequences, the CEO (or a manager at any level) might better reach decisions and prepare for possible consequences. Being selectively inclusive, along with voicing appreciation for thoughts conveyed by others, enriches the work environment, strengthening loyalty to both manager and mission. After benefiting from such inclusiveness, a huge mistake one can make is to take sole personal credit for a decision's successful result. It is a failure to understand that one gains in both stature and loyalty upon recognizing others for their contributions.

An administrative action may not please everyone involved in the discussions leading to its implementation, but it is important employees involved know their views have been considered and come to appreciate over time that while they may not prevail on every issue, they do influence favorably a fair share of decisions, and when not, understand why. Any such explanation should be done before broadcast of the decision, to reassure dissenters they were indeed heard and understood.

---

[11] https://www.brainyquote.com/quotes/donald_rumsfeld_148142. Accessed 1 October 2018.

Opinions surveyed may be widely divergent and make decision difficult, but temporizing by the CEO can only make things worse. And the executive who repeatedly agrees with whomever was last in the office invites disaster.

The late W. Edwards Deming[12] opined that when relevant new observations or data improve or challenge existing knowledge or theory, they must be evaluated objectively without rigid commitment to prior judgment. In the care of patients, that's how the physician deals with new diagnostic information or a change in the patient's condition. The same should be true for any organization's manager. New knowledge can offer new perspective and, one hopes, a more informed course of action and better outcome.

In medicine some decisions must be made without delay, but others warrant more deliberate a process when needed information may not be immediately apparent. At times it may be better to do nothing than take a "shot in the dark." It's a rare physician, if any, who never made a clinical judgment that, in retrospect, he or she wishes a different choice had been reached. An alternative might have been better, although not necessarily so — there are no *a priori* guarantees. Regret arises, or at least the nagging thought that another choice might have been better. Medicine is not a perfect science, nor does any individual practitioner exemplify perfection. The same is true for management in business and its decision-makers.

Savoring one's management decisions well-made tends to be ephemeral, but the memory of one proven wrong churns forever. At decision time, it may have been perceived as best, but in retrospect, not so as its consequences unfold, even when other choices seemed less palatable. Just as a good decision, whether medical or management, can favorably influence the fate of a patient or an organization, a decision less than optimal may do the opposite. The impact can range from minor to major, with unforeseen and regretful consequences.

---

[12] Deming WE. Out of the Crisis. Massachusetts Institute of Technology, Center for Advanced Engineering Study. Cambridge, Massachusetts. 1982.

Reflecting on actions later wished I'd made differently, I feel they were not done in haste but made with less deliberation or fewer facts gathered than later I felt warranted. Mine to make as responsible clinician or organization manager, they remain my responsibility. It was not simply more time needed for thoughtful decision-making; it was the need for further dispassionate and informed consideration of the complexity of the issue and its possible outcomes.

As a resident in internal medicine, I witnessed an impressive example of diligent exploration of knowns and unknowns where a critical decision had to be made. A woman in her eighties, essentially healthy, was admitted to the hospital having ruptured a diverticulum in her colon. That meant there was a small hole in her large bowel, and fecal contents could be leaking into the peritoneal cavity, her abdomen. That led to her abdominal pain and fever. The indicated treatment would be surgery to repair the leak, clean out the peritoneal cavity, and expect that things would move back to normal under a regimen of antibiotics and IV fluids.

But there was another issue, one of prime importance to the patient. She had been looking forward eagerly to attend the debut of a beloved granddaughter, a major event for her and her Southern family. The debut was to be several days hence. Were she operated on now, the trip, debut, and long anticipated family gathering would be missed, a huge disappointment. For over an hour, I watched two senior physicians — one a GI surgeon and the other a medical gastroenterologist — go back and forth discussing options and consequences possible. Should we ignore the debut and the patient's great disappointment and do "what's right," or could we risk it, treat her with antibiotics, a careful regimen of hydration, limit food by mouth, hope that her symptoms would be held in check for several days in the hospital, then send her off, continuing with antibiotics and a limited diet — with fingers crossed until she returned from the event for her needed surgery. For me it was like watching a tennis match — the ball went back and forth between these two experienced clinicians until there were no further considerations to discuss, no more insights to be summoned.

Ultimately they reached agreement to delay the surgery, monitor the patient in hospital for several days, and if she were to do well, offer a cautious bon voyage for her trip, along with detailed advice on what to do routinely and what to do if her health did not go well. Several days post-discharge, the patient returned medically stable as hoped for, immensely gratified to have been at the event. She then did well at surgery. It could have gone a different way — there was no guarantee of successful outcome. But the judgment to help the patient achieve her long-anticipated important goal came only after thoughtful consideration of all the known and unknown issues uncoverable — medical, social, and personal — thoughtfully worked through by the patient and her two physicians.

I still mull over medical decisions I made that led to less than optimal outcome. A different choice might have offered a better result. Also, as a hospital CEO, I reflect on administrative choices that led to suboptimal results. While the forward thrust of the hospital was not reversed, there were aspects of its complex functioning that lost ground for a time. Better consideration of causation and possible consequences would have been wiser. I should have engaged more thoroughly with institutional colleagues, and for some decisions, with reliable external advisors to extend my reach of the knowns and unknowns. I should have explored more critically my reasoning. For those decisions, the responsibility remains mine, along with unending regret over lack of the more thoughtful consideration I might have employed.

Thinking further about the "knowns and unknowns," it strikes me that the phrase relates more to external considerations than to the thinking processes of those making the decision. There is another component in decision-making, one long thought about by educators but only recently considered in medicine and perhaps less so in organization management. It is meta-cognition, self-examination of clarity and objectivity of cognition by decision-makers, carried out through one's personal capacity and candor to explore his/her own mind-set and biases.

Critical thinking and meta-cognition should be a part of any major decision-making process. To examine one's own thinking processes could retrieve some of the "unknown unknowns" into the "known knowns" category and render the ultimate decision more informed. This is more than self-scrutiny of one's possible biases; it is a search within one's self to examine how clearly and objectively one is thinking on an issue.

In a 2007 issue of The New Yorker, Dr. Jerome Groopman[13] offered several examples in medicine where lapses in critical thinking and critical reasoning could lead to misdiagnosis. He characterized the fault as less attention than needed to the "cognitive dimension of clinical decision-making." Citing the work of Pat Crosskerry, M.D.,[14] then in charge of the Emergency Room at Dartmouth Hospital in Halifax, Nova Scotia, Groopman gives several examples of errors made by physicians.

- "Representativeness." Thinking is overly influenced by what is typically true. The failure to consider possibilities that contradict one's mental templates of a disease and thus attribute symptoms to a wrong cause.
- "Availability." The tendency to judge the likelihood of an event by the ease with which (seemingly) relevant examples come to mind.
- "Confirmation Bias." Confirming what one expects to find by selectively accepting or ignoring information.

Patients, too, may fail in their thinking. Examples might be insistence on one's surgery to be done by the once distinguished but now aged surgeon formerly hailed as an expert (and possibly a close friend

---

[13] Groopman J. newyorker.com/magazine/2007/01/29/whats-the-trouble. Accessed 3 May2019.
[14] Crosskerry P. Achieving quality in clinical decision making: Cognitive strategies and detection of bias. Acad Emerg Med. 2002;9(11):1184-1204.

of the patient) but now long out of the competence once enjoyed, or reliance on the recounting by a friend or prominent individual of his/her choice of treatment for a disorder that may or may not be related to the clinical issue at hand.

Groopman concludes, as Tversky and Kahneman[15] and other cognitive psychologists have shown, when people are confronted with uncertainty — the situation of every doctor attempting to diagnose a patient — they are susceptible to unconscious emotions and personal biases and are more likely to make cognitive errors. Crosskerry believes that the first step toward incorporating an awareness of heuristics (how one makes judgments and decisions in the face of complex issues or incomplete information) in medical practice is to recognize that how doctors think can affect their success as much as their fund of readily accessed knowledge or the extent of their experience.

Tversky and Kahnemann conclude, "A better understanding of these heuristics and of the biases to which they lead could improve judgment and decisions in situations of uncertainty." Fortunately, critical thinking is increasingly appreciated as important for improved performance by health care professionals in this contemporary era of information overload. Its understanding and use are now becoming incorporated into medical education and the training of young physicians.[16] Shouldn't the same hold true for its use by managers in business?

BEING CEO

"TAKING CONTROL"

More than once I've been asked this question, "Given that you were quite young — not yet thirty-six — when you took over at Beth Israel Hospital, how did you 'take control?'"

---

[15] Tversky A, Kahnemann D. Judgment under uncertainty. Heuristic biases. Pp 35-52. In Connolly T., Arkes HR, Hammond KR, eds. Judgment and decision making. An interdisciplinary reader. Cambridge, UK. Cambridge University Press. 2000.
[16] Huang GC, Newman LR, Schwartzstein RM. Critical thinking in health professions education. Summary and consensus statements of the Millennium Conference 2011. Teach Learn Med. 2014;26(1):95-102.

Fact is I never thought about it in that way. I was singularly fortunate on arrival. The Chief Operating Officer, Jack Kasten, had a degree in law and one in bacteriology, along with sound administrative experience, good sense, a broad knowledge of hospital operation, the health care scene in Boston, and beyond. My first mentor, he was welcoming and generous. If he felt he should have been the CEO, there was no inkling of it. I remain deeply grateful to him. Many others were helpful, and I needed all they generously gave. The department chairs in medicine, surgery, and pathology, Drs. Howard Hiatt, William Silen, and David Freiman, and other physicians, too, were supportive; I knew many of them as fellow Harvard Medical School faculty members.

There were dissenting views. Years later I was told of a comment bandied about shortly after my arrival, "We'll have him gone in three weeks." It may have represented honest skepticism more than opposition, as another incident illustrated. Some weeks after my arrival, which coincided with that of Dr. Silen as chair of surgery, several physicians met with the board chair, Irving Rabb, voicing strong doubts over changes both of us were making, ultimately urging that he fire us both.

Mr. Rabb's answer was a quick, "No. Now what else should we talk about?" Some years later, the same physicians met with me as we began seeking a new chair in medicine. Their conversation went something like this. "Mitch, you share our values about quality of care and academic scholarship. The choice of a new professor of medicine is critical for BI. We need a great clinician, a fine scientist, great teacher, and role model. We need someone like Bill Silen."

Every CEO shapes a reputation from arrival. Events in the workplace or in the public eye help form an image of the new arrival. Several things I did in the first days, not planned, may have helped shape initial views of this freshman CEO. The hospital gift shop didn't sell chewing gum because, I was told, some "abc gum" (already been chewed) gets deposited on corridor floors and is not that easy to clean up. The decision seemed reasonable but by contrast, I felt, our gift shop sale of cigarettes was not. Asking its sale be stopped, I noted in a newsletter my inability to understand how an institution devoted to the prevention and treatment of illness could be selling these harbingers of disease, disability, and death. Several years later after repeated voicings of the dangers of tobacco, it took an active process of some months to create a smoke-free institution and surrounding grounds, illustrating one difference in dealing with an inanimate product versus human behavior.

I took early action on another issue. A segment of the cafeteria was walled off by a folding screen to serve as "doctors dining area." Rarely was it even halfway occupied while the rest of the cafeteria was crowded. With removal of the folding doors, I stated we all were engaged in the care of patients, one way or another, and it was not appropriate to hold seats vacant in one corner of the cafeteria when others could not be seated elsewhere. There was no kickback.

Neither decision was done with thought of "taking control." Perhaps they conveyed such, but that was not the intent. Another incident, accidental, may have had more impact. Having gotten a letter of complaint about the care of a patient, I went to that unit to chat with the nursing staff. The patient's surgeon was known to be imperious, well-regarded in the lay community but highly authoritarian. In the hospital, he brooked no interference, and few would dare doubt, much less contradict him. The nursing station was crowded with medical students, interns and residents, nurses, and several physicians. I had opened the patient's medical record just as his surgeon happened to appear. It was a paper medical record and before today's HIPAA (Health Insurance Portability and Accountability Act) privacy rules about who can access a patient's data.

"Rabkin," he orated in commanding tones, "what are you doing looking at my patient's record?" I wish I could state my response was consciously developed, but it just came out.

"Dr.___, in this hospital, they are all my patients." The sudden silence in the room was coupled with the whooshed intake of many breaths. The surgeon turned, left without a word, and people went back to their tasks.

Word may have spread that I don't take guff from anyone and was taking control. "Control" implies that an individual is ascribed by others to have power that commands. The fact is that power is assigned by others. If people fail to respond to directions or suggestions by an individual formally invested with authority over them (or in any group where authority may be assumed by one of them), that individual truly is powerless. One cannot be a leader if no one follows. Leadership does not inevitably derive from vignettes like those cited above, whether consciously enacted in an effort to establish dominance or occurring by happenstance. The issue is not dominance. Leadership is earned by describing the reality facing the organization, articulating its mission, vision, goals, and the work to fulfil them in ways that elicit understanding, loyalty, and commitment, and then working to support the success of those she or he is charged to lead.

BEING CEO

ON VIEW

Early in my time at Beth Israel, one of our trustees, Mr. Max Feldberg, then in his late seventies, dropped by the office and asked if I had a few minutes to spend with him.

"Let's take a walk," he offered. We headed to a patient unit. Pointing to scattered bits of litter in the corridor, he asked, "Why do you think there's this stuff on the floor?"

My response, "It's because people are so messy."

"You're a scientist," he said. "Let's do an experiment. We'll walk down this corridor and pick up alternate pieces of litter. Then we'll go upstairs to a comparable unit and see what's there." Together we then bent down to pick up about half of what was scattered on the floor. One floor above there was (statistically speaking) a comparable distribution of litter; we touched nothing.

On returning to the first floor of our encounter, most we had left untouched had been picked up. "You see," Mr. Max said, "it's not because people are messy. It's because you are! If you're so fancy, you can't bend down to pick up trash, why should anybody else?"

His question had widespread consequences. When the CEO is seen by employees in informal day-to-day circumstances, invariably he or she is observed, interpreted, privately commented on, and perhaps reacted to. In this instance, there seemed little room for misinterpretation. My efforts became widely known as I continued to pick up trash, increasing skill in both lay-ups and long shots into a wastebasket. It became okay for others to do so, and the hospital grew close to litter-free.

Some time later my wife happened to drop by the hospital. We encountered David Dolins, Chief Operating Officer, as we climbed a stairway. As each of us spotted a bit of litter, Adrienne bent to pick it up, but David unhesitatingly countered, "Please hold off, this is my stairway for litter."

Another funny incident arose out of my now ingrained habit. Inured to even the most fetid of litter, there was virtually nothing I wouldn't pick up. I returned to my office one morning to meet someone new to both the hospital and me.

He rose, "Good morning, Dr. Rabkin," extending his hand.

"Excuse me a moment," I replied. "I have to wash my hands."

As I disappeared into the nearby washroom, he whispered to Susan Lubars, my executive assistant, "Just how long has he had this hand-washing fetish?"

There's more to the emphasis on hand-washing than obsessive neatness, particularly so in hospitals where anyone can spread germs to patients and staff. Today antibacterial hand lotion dispensers are stationed throughout hospitals and clinics, and staff nationally are fairly good about their use, although a thorough hand washing with soap does as well. Clean hands concern everyone, including visitors.

We encouraged patients to ask their doctors, nurses, and others, "Have you washed your hands?" With a growing percentage of bacteria developing resistance even to the latest antibiotics, the importance of preventing infection is prime, and needed control measures extend beyond hand-washing to range from scrub suits and face masks to stethoscopes, other medical and nursing equipment, and even doctors' neckties. As we learned in the current SARS-CoV-2 pandemic, there still is a way to go.

BEING CEO

THE OUTSIDE WORLD

Visibility extends beyond the hospital. Most of us, executives or not, are on display well beyond our own bailiwick. My wife and I were dining at a restaurant where booths existed side-by-side, separated by a wall that did not reach the ceiling. Conversation seemed to drift from one booth to the other, usually fragments but at other times the whole package.

We were startled to overhear, "You know what Rabkin thinks? I'll tell you what Rabkin thinks." There followed a huge misrepresentation of my thoughts, motivations, and intentions. I was tempted to jump up, loom over the barrier separating the booths, and "straighten out" the speaker. Rationality prevailed and we polished off dinner knowing that misrepresentation by others may be simply a fact of life, and denial less effective than one's actions.

A different dinner underscored that one is always on display, recognizable or not. At a restaurant in Boston's Chinatown, we noticed a family of four several tables distant. One parent was a brilliant psychoanalyst, exquisitely perceptive, remarkably calm in the most explosive of therapeutic encounters, eminently effective as therapist, teacher, and role model. But here with family, over egg foo young, the friction and noise among them shared equally but led by that parent offered rather different a view of this appropriately celebrated therapist. We're all human.

A useful lesson came from an unexpected source. Years ago in a cost-cutting effort, the Massachusetts Bay Transportation Authority decided to limit operating hours for several Boston bus routes. These were busses used by many of our kitchen work force and housekeepers. If carried out, among other impacts, the change would lead to hours of delay for patients' breakfasts, unacceptable to patients, and disruptive of hospital operations.

At a public hearing on the proposed changes, I went to object. Coming down with flu that evening, I felt rotten, had a fever, severe headache, and muscle aches but was determined to argue against the proposed changes and give my reasons why. Managing to say my thing, I headed home and to bed. A bit of my testimony was shown on the TV news later that evening.

Feeling better in a few days and heading for the hospital, I stopped for gasoline. At that time, attendants were pumping gas. Filling the tank, he wagged his finger at me.

"What's the problem?" I asked.

"Doc," he said, "I saw you on TV. You was terrible."

"What do you mean?" I replied.

His answer, "So serious."

"Well, it was serious," I countered. "If they had cut the bus service, our folks wouldn't have gotten to the hospital in time to make breakfast for the patients."

"Look, Doc, you know it's serious. I know it's serious. But the average guy out there in TV land, he don't know from serious. I don't care what it is. He takes one look at your face and says, 'The son-of-a-bitch deserves it.' Doc, you got to smile and then they'll say, 'They're screwin' the poor bastard.'"

The medium is indeed the message, I thought, smiling on my way to the hospital.

BEING CEO
ADVERSE EVENTS

Occasionally a physician or nurse may hesitate to be open about an adverse event. In the care of patients, when something untoward happens, physicians and nurses feel badly. We're all human; no one is perfect. Mistakes can occur more frequently than some believed, fortunately less so now with greater attention to their identification and prevention. In each instance, bad outcome or not, adverse events must be identified and examined for causation, whether human or systems fallibility or the not unexpected natural course of an illness. Just as physicians have learned that glossing over the fact of a dismal prognosis is usually the wrong thing to do, transparency about adverse events is critically important to determine their causes and prevent their future occurrence.

Some years ago, a physician at our hospital administered the wrong drug to a patient. Two syringes contained separate medications, properly labelled, one to be administered by a route differing from that for the other. Inadvertently the first injection went by the route the second should have taken. Instantly recognizing what was likely a lethal error, the physician double-checked for possible consequences and remedies. With heavy heart but complete candor and no delay, the physician told colleagues and chief what had happened and then shared the details and likely consequences with the patient and family. Not easy, these were the right things to do.

In such situations, the hospital's risk management office and legal counsel are notified immediately. They speak with all involved, counsel on what can be said, by whom, and hospital management sequesters the patient's medical record, operative and anesthesia notes, relevant medical equipment, drug vials (even if empty), IV bottles and equipment, etc., for further scrutiny. That is not to hide mistakes but to be sure that all possibly related evidence, whether material or documentation, remains unaltered and held untouched and securely for subsequent dispassionate and objective review.

In this instance, it was felt, appropriately, that both patient and family should be informed and given medical and emotional support. Counseling and support were also given to the physician, a competent and experienced clinician deeply distressed by the error. As anticipated the patient died in the hospital several days later. It was traumatic, sobering not only for the patient and family and physician but for many throughout the hospital. It would have been wrong to have handled the situation with less candor.

As CEO I met with the patient's large family explaining the error and how it took place, told them of the training and otherwise unblemished performance of the involved physician, and voiced my sincere regret, that of others involved and our apologies. I described the support we gave the patient and immediate family during the last few days of life and detailed what we now were changing, so that such an error would not be repeated.

I had been aware of a highly publicized earlier instance in another city. It was in no way parallel to ours. Although the responsibility for that patient's death had not been identified definitively, one physician involved had been pressured to leave the medical profession. Deeming that outcome less than fair, I did not want it to happen here and insisted that our involved physician resume work the following day. I did so, feeling that the physician would never repeat such an error. Greater good would result from that outcome, along with counseling and support, than loss to the profession of an excellent doctor.

At times mistakes can relate to systems' problems and not human error. When two drugs with closely similar names are provided in similar-looking containers, or the labeling of medication names and dosages are less easily read than other information on the bottles, it is understandable how one might be confused for the other, especially in hurried circumstances. Examples of other errors include when two or more participants slip up in performing and documenting their parts in a prescribed sequence of events or when a check list on a pre-operative patient is not reviewed simultaneously by surgeon, operating room nurse, and anesthesiologist.

The multi-authored report by the Institute of Medicine (now National Academy of Medicine[17]) highlighted its extensive eye-opening inquiry, "Two large studies, one conducted in Colorado and Utah, and the other in New York, found that adverse events occurred in 2.9 and 3.2 percent of hospitalizations respectively. In Colorado and Utah hospitals, 6.6 percent of adverse events led to death, as compared with 13.6 percent in New York hospitals. In both of these studies, over half of these adverse events resulted from medical errors and could have been prevented." The preface of their report anticipates its conclusion, "Errors can be prevented by designing systems that make it hard for people to do the wrong thing and easy for people to do the right thing." Today administrators, physicians, and nurses anticipate preventing adverse events, even identifying and correcting errors yet to be made, that is, situations where an existing process might make for future error. This approach is inherited in part from the work of W. Edwards Deming,[12] who revolutionized the notion of quality by emphasizing that identifying "rejects" at the end of a production line — products that do not meet the quality standards — does nothing to resolve the problem of producing such rejects. One has to examine the *process* of production to identify its possible defects and make corrective changes in that process itself. These insights were adopted early in aviation and led to realization that identifying systems' solutions was more productive than seeking an individual to blame and banning him or her from the cockpit. Important steps taken today at hospitals include a check list, reviewed not by one person alone but together by several, or repeatedly asking for the patient's name and birth date by each caregiver contacting the patient and matching that with the information on the patient's wrist bracelet and specific medications. This redundancy was also drawn from aviation where pilot and co-pilot together carry out a detailed review on which to agree before the aircraft can be deemed ready to fly.

---

[17] Kohn LT, Corrigan JM, Donaldson MS. To Err is Human: Building a Safer Health System. Washington, DC. Institute of Medicine, National Academy Press. 2000.

BEING CEO
APPEAL OF PERFORMANCE JUDGMENT

Should any worker feel he or she is unjustly accused of deficiency in carrying out hospital policy, airing that employee's view of criticism voiced by his/her manager offers a useful bulwark against unfair judgment. We made resolution easy through our Appeals Policy and Procedure. Used to seek review of a manager's decision felt unjustified or unfair, whether from performance review or otherwise (if not resolved through the assistance of Human Resources staff), the employee begins by seeking resolution with the manager who made that judgment. If the manager's reviewed decision was felt to be unacceptable, the employee can give notice to the manager that he/she wants to pursue the issue through the hospital's Appeal Procedure. The employee should be clear about the nature of the grievance and what relief is sought; the manager must be clear on why he/she chose the position appealed against.

At the first hearing is the appellant with an advisor he/she may select; the manager against whose decision the employee is appealing, and that manager's manager, who will hear and decide on the matter, and upon request of any party, a Human Resources specialist. Witnesses may be called by any party but remain only long enough to give their testimony. Decision at the end of the hearing will emerge from the facts and opinions made available. Then if either party wishes to appeal the resulting decision to the next upward level of management, he/she may do so. A similar process is then repeated serially up to the hospital CEO, who may assemble a group of individuals to consider the issues raised, review hospital policies involved, and make recommendations toward fair resolution of the matter.

These recommendations will be reviewed by a five-person task force:

- Two full-time employees of the hospital chosen by the employee making the appeal.
- The manager with whom the employee has the grievance.

- A representative of the administration designated by the CEO.
- A full-time employee of the hospital chosen at large by and in mutual agreement of the four individuals listed above.

There will also be a non-voting member appointed by the Vice President, Human Resources from the Department of Human Resources to assist in clarifying hospital policy, personnel records, etc., as needed. The chair of the fact-finding committee shall be chosen by and from the voting members.

The fact-finding committee is charged to review without bias the grievance of the employee from all relevant written material, including that from both employee and manager, and from discussion with each of them, with other employees the appealing employee may choose to have help him or her, and with others deemed appropriate by the committee. The appeal and fact-finding procedure will be carried out in a diligent but informal, impartial, and non-judicial atmosphere. After as thorough a review as possible, the committee will come to its recommendation by majority vote.

The CEO reviews the committee's recommendation and concludes the proceedings with a final decision. Throughout my tenure as CEO, of up to six to eight such appeals annually reaching me, final decisions favored employees and managers each about fifty percent of the time.

BEING CEO
ONCE I HUNG UP ON A PATIENT
No, it wasn't a patient, it was a daughter of the patient, an elderly man in hospital with terminal illness. Two daughters there were, both in their sixties, whom it appeared he had long compelled to be his caretakers. Neither had married nor ventured occupationally or socially, both bound fully to meeting his needs as far as one could surmise. For them nothing we did was satisfactory. They complained constantly, berating nurses, doctors, my office staff, and me.

What was taking place? To me it seemed likely these women carried suppressed anger over decades at this demanding father. Fury such as theirs, psychiatrists comment, can be accompanied by unconscious wishes for death of the person creating their miserable situation. Now the moment was approaching. Could that provoke sharp feelings of guilt as if the persons harboring those suppressed wishes were doing the deed themselves?

One of the ways such feelings are handled is through projecting one's guilt onto others. Were these daughters loading their unconscious guilt onto us? Repeatedly I assured them their father's care was appropriate, everything clinically possible was being done and done well. I emphasized they, too, had done everything, even more than expected. Nothing tempered their outbursts.

About 3 A.M. one night, my home phone rang. It was one of the sisters yelling that a medication scheduled for 2:30 A.M. had not been given until 2:45. She went on to voice more complaints. I noticed my two children, seven and ten, peeking around the bedroom door with eyes widening as I hung up after saying,

"Madam, I will not speak with you further. You can come to my office in the morning and we'll continue the discussion."

The kids had never seen me speak curtly to a patient or family. I tried to explain how difficult these two sisters were, but the children seemed hesitant to buy it. Again the phone rang. It was the other sister yelling loudly enough, so the children caught her message.

"Did you just hang up on my sister?"

My reply, "Yes, madam, and I'm hanging up on you! Goodbye." Perhaps more convinced of my view, the kids returned to bed.

Earlier that evening, the daughters had raised another scene on the nursing unit. On the following morning, I went up to calm the waters.

A nurse greeted me, "I guess you're going to chew us out about last night with the family—"

"Not at all," I replied, "but let's chat about it." I asked the nurses whether they knew the difference between a dog and a cat; they were baffled. I went on, "Take a dog you know, point your finger, scowl and say, 'You bad dog!' and the dog might shrink. Try that on a cat; it doesn't work. The dog seems to know guilt, but the cat doesn't. Just because a patient or family member wants you to feel guilty doesn't mean you're obliged to do so. Sure, if we make a mistake, we should be candid about it. Complaints can alert us to possible problems with systems or people. But if it appears someone may be projecting their own guilt onto you, don't take offense. You're a clinician. Be objective about the issue, but consider possible psychology underlying the complaint. Respond fairly and with understanding, but neither your professional judgment nor your response should be overcome by the emotional intensity of the complainer. If guilt is being projected on you, be more like a cat than a dog. Deal with the complaint's substance objectively and be as supportive as possible. That's our professional responsibility."

Most patients and families who complain to us are willing to continue with the doctors, nurses, and hospital involved. They want a reasonable response and feasible appropriate changes. But those who register complaints only to others keep us unaware of something that could possibly be improved. Even if the complaint were trivial or unwarranted, we can be honest in voicing thanks for alerting us to the voiced concern. Input of all kinds from patients and families helps improve performance.

CHAPTER 5: LESSONS LEARNED

CRITICAL INCIDENTS AND APPEALS

The transition from clinician to corporate manager demands much that's new to the novice. Among these is importance of well-done performance review. Subordinates need to know for what specifically they are accountable — its nature, quality, quantity, and timing, and the limits of freedom they have to act independently. When these are defined and understood, the person being reviewed should be able to open his or her review session with a thoughtful response to the request, "Tell me how you feel you're doing in your role." By contrast if a worker is handed little more than the role's title and an unclear mandate, no grounds exist for criticism of performance. When role description is unclear or performance evaluation superficial, future problems can loom.

I learned to keep a "critical incident file" to document performance of immediate subordinates. It included notable performance, positive and negative, proving useful to justify my decision to favor or caution an employee. On occasion I might anticipate a conflict between what I said and what the person being reviewed might have felt had taken place in a counseling or warning session.

To document any such discussion, I would write a memo describing our dialog and add, "If the content noted here differs from what you feel took place in our (specifically dated) meeting, get back to me in writing with your understanding, and please do so without delay." Usually there was no response. My written summary of our discussion, along with proposed recommendations or actions noted, would serve as basis for subsequent conversations recognizing improvement or voicing further concern. When I interacted with physicians who were not hospital employees, a similar approach applied, though remedies, depending on the circumstances, might proceed under medical staff by-laws rather than through hospital human resource policies.

SOME LESSONS LEARNED
A SOLUTION IS NOT ALWAYS THE SOLUTION

Experts advise the executive to handle a piece of paper only once. Take definitive action and be done with it. It's comforting to do that, but the underlying issue may not readily be apparent at first blush. What may surface as a simple problem with seeming ready solution can mask an unspoken issue of greater complexity.

Early in my tenure, several house officers (interns and residents) asked to meet with me. They seemed mildly agitated though their problem was simple — lack of stirrups on a certain exam table.

"How can we do an adequate pelvic exam?" asked one. He was correct. This could easily be resolved. Fully sympathetic I responded with a phone call: stirrups were found and placed. The house officers left, seeming satisfied.

Several days later, a message from the same house officers brought ten new complaints, coupled with hints of anger toward me. None had been mentioned previously. I didn't understand it, having dealt instantly with their initial complaint (unusual for the CEO even to have been confronted with it and even more so to have responded directly), I found them back with me again. Why had appropriate channels for such issues been avoided? And why the anger toward me?

Later that day, I happened to be chatting with a board member, a psychoanalyst and student of leadership. He suggested my straightforward consideration of the initial complaint may have missed the real issue. Could we explore possibilities of what might underlie their voiced concerns? Despite its apparent solution, he explained, a complaint sometimes masks a deeper issue, hesitant to articulate, perhaps even unconscious. We considered a possibility the house officers were angry not with me but were displacing through anger toward me frustration that might not readily be directed where it properly applied.

We understood these house officers had joined the department attracted by the character of its chief. Charismatic, he focused on biomedical science and its impact on clinical medicine. These young physicians may have envisioned research as a prominent component of their careers, just as their chief exemplified. But recently he announced a sabbatical year away from the hospital. Would that deprive these house officers of the personal leadership they had envisioned? Even more concerning, we speculated, he had spoken of a shift in his scholarly direction. Recognizing that prevention might do more for community health than does curative medicine, he would focus on public health during the sabbatical. And on return, he would try to apply rigorous scientific methodologies of biomedical research to study and action in public health. To the house officers, might his new focus augur loss of what had attracted them to join his department? Might their anger come from feelings of abandonment? It is never easy for interns and residents to recriminate against their chief of service. Future promotions and recommendations are in the offing. Anger is more readily displaced elsewhere.

Our discussion seemed worth a try for resolution. If the underlying feelings were abandonment, my challenge was to offer the situation's possible psychodynamics to their chief and help him implement its solution. The sabbatical leave would not be cancelled, nor his odyssey into public health. But how to do this? Clearly, he would have to deal with the house officers' issues, reinforcing his role as their continuing leader. He would not fail in supporting their experience as residents or their future career goals, however his and theirs might evolve. Offering that I had jumped too fast in dealing with the stirrups, I saw that being the good "grandfather" can pull the rug out from under the "father," weakening his stature only to compound the unconscious resentment.

The chief and I were at a medical meeting a few days later. Held in Atlantic City, it gave us the opportunity together to walk the length of the boardwalk several times over. With no hesitation, he recognized the possible feeling of abandonment by the house officers and the need to counter it. He would deal with the ten complaints recently handed to me.

Back in Boston, he met with the group. Having discussed their issues with me, he reported he had looked into them.

"Seven of the ten," he told them, "I have resolved. On another I secured a halfway solution, and the other two could not be altered for valid reasons (that he explained). But we got seven-and-a-half out of ten." He went on to chat about other issues, including his sabbatical leave, adding reassurance of his support to them for their anticipated futures. The change in the house officers was impressive. From resentment they could not voice directly, the air was cleared. The balance of the year went well, the sabbatical leave led to growth in the chief's career, and the house officers went on to their own achievements.

This episode offered an example of how a "simple" issue — a clear complaint with seeming straightforward solution — turns out to be a metaphor for a significant but unspoken problem. I learned to become more alert to possible "real" issues hiding under the table. While others might hesitate to bring them to the fore, a CEO cannot allow these to fester, even though it may not be wise at a particular moment to put a hidden agenda on table top. Sooner or later though, one must get at it.

SOME LESSONS LEARNED

A PROBLEM WORKER IS NOT ALWAYS THE PROBLEM

Over my time as CEO at Beth Israel Hospital, two unsuccessful attempts were made to unionize employees. During the first, I wondered why one or two departments seemed to contain almost exclusively the rabid pro-union employees while most workers elsewhere showed little interest.

I asked our consultant, Tony McKeown, "Why is it that all the wild ones seem to be located in these two departments?" His response was meaningful not only for thinking about our union drive. It highlighted an important reason why unions might or might not be right for an organization.

"It isn't that all those 'wild ones' are in one department or another because they were recruited there," he responded. "When a problem of this nature surfaces, the first thing to think about is the department's manager."

Tony was right. On thorough review, we concluded that both managers were less than competent for the roles they occupied, and once they were replaced, a world of difference followed. More than three decades later, several of those employees among the most outspoken remained in those same departments, continuing as solid performers.

Tony's counsel went beyond importance of good managers and the need to replace those lacking. His lesson was that to avoid unionization is to avoid employees' need for unionization. That is, to operate the organization in a manner that meets employees' needs, material, and human. If you can do that, unions offer little else. That's not being invariably against unions, it is being invariably for sound management, thoughtful leadership, and fair treatment with solid human resource policy and performance. Happily, with Laura Avakian and her assistant, Maria Tarullo, heading Human Resources, we were able to do that.

SOME LESSONS LEARNED
ANY QUESTIONS?

Presenting to a group of managers or their employees, were you ever confronted with a sea of blank faces and no response to, "Do you have any questions?" It happened to me, more on issues presented to second-tier managers who then were to share the information with their workers, than when welcoming new employees at any level. By contrast, discussion with my vice-presidents was not one-sided. They never hesitated asking questions, voicing disagreement or confusion, improving understanding all around. Why the difference in response?

A colleague, I don't remember who — suggested that when I ask, "Any questions?" perhaps I was implying, "Who is so thick they don't understand my perfectly clear comments?" Instead of "Any questions?" I changed my approach, "Now when you're talking about this with your employees, what questions do you think they might ask?"

Many would then open up, voicing doubts, potential misunderstandings, even disagreements their employees might raise. The new dialog would bring about greater detail, new insights on the issue and its implications. It's no surprise that people don't welcome a hint, though unintended, that they may not be savvy enough to understand. The ensuing discussions added clarity to the managers' understanding and their sensitivity to the responses they might get from their workers. I, too, might gain insight previously missed.

SOME LESSONS LEARNED
GOOD INTENTIONS ALONE ARE NOT ENOUGH

On the street directly outside the hospital's emergency unit, a pedestrian was leveled by a passing auto. The ER was alerted, and several staff headed out with a gurney for the victim. After brief evaluation, they brought her to the unit for further review. Fortunately, she was soon able to be released. Several hours later, I was alerted to the episode, learning of two employees who reached the victim on the street. In my next newsletter, I commended both for their prompt and helpful response. A day later, two other employees came to see me. They, too, had been involved in the "rescue." Why, they asked, had I failed to mention them? I could only apologize, having been too hasty to voice commendations before getting full details of the event. Admitting my error, I noted them and their efforts in the following newsletter.

It was a lesson I should have remembered from an embarrassing episode years earlier. A huge snowstorm was predicted, promising to become problematic for hospital patients needing to arrive and those about to be discharged and for our own employees and medical staff. Anticipating the emergency, I elected to stay overnight, and arrangements were made for on-site staff who elected to do the same. By morning the city was thickly blanketed in snow. Only the National Guard in special vehicles were able to navigate, confining their efforts largely to trips for women in labor and the occasional medical emergency.

Some of the staff who had trudged to nearby homes the night before would not be able to make it back that morning, but with those who had stayed overnight, basic functions could be carried out. Thinking of various sites in the hospital, I considered the creatures in our research animal quarters. Surely, I reasoned, the employees attending them would be delayed at best, perhaps even unavailable for a day or more. Food and water were critical. Without further inquiry, I decided the animals would be my responsibility that morning.

I began with the several dogs we had. From their response to the offered food, it seemed they were eager for a late breakfast. Most smaller animals tend to nibble at their supply of food from time to time and they seemed to have some available from yesterday. Water levels varied from cage to cage, so they were refilled. Satisfied with my effort, I returned to my office for other issues of the day.

An hour later, two employees walked into my office. They were animal caretakers and pressed to speak with me. Welcoming them I assumed they had just arrived through the snow and wanted to thank me for my helpful effort.

"Doc," they admonished with some passion, "don't you ever go into the animal farm again!" I learned that around midnight both had started trudging back from their homes some eight to ten miles away, arriving in time to feed and care for all the animals before I came on scene, at which point they had gone to the cafeteria for breakfast. (If you have ever owned one, you'll know that even after a full meal, few dogs will not welcome more.) My benighted effort had led to diarrhea for several of the animals, inappropriately adding to the caretakers' work that morning. Fortunately, I did not ruin any studies involving the animals. I could only apologize, assuring them I would be hands off from then on.

The commitment they showed to their responsibilities contrasted sharply with my ill-considered "helpfulness." It reminded me of the corollary admonition, "Be sure brain is engaged before putting mouth in gear."

SOME LESSONS LEARNED
THE GARAGE CAPER — A SPECTACULAR FAILURE

In the early eighties, a host of patients alerted me that the hospital's then only parking garage was too crowded. Unable to find a spot, some turned away. A few claimed they would seek medical care elsewhere. Something had to be done. I huddled with our vice-presidents. With seventy-five employees using the garage, we reasoned that if half the group were placed elsewhere, the immediate crisis could be handled. The question was, which half were to leave?

Debated at our weekly top management meeting were criteria to be used. Some argued on the basis of employment longevity. None felt those higher on the organizational hierarchy should be spared while those lower should depart. Other proposals aired over five weeks led to settling on a lottery system. Parkers would draw numbers from one to seventy-five, and it would be happenstance who would park elsewhere, except for the few with disability. Numbers one through thirty-seven would vacate while thirty-eight to seventy-five would stay. And were any of those remaining in the garage to leave employment, we would have a logical sequence beginning with number one for return of those outplaced. Without announcing it, I also elected to join those displaced.

We felt this decision fair, considerate to employees at all levels, and consistent with the human resource philosophy of our hospital. Certain of ready acceptance, I asked the vice-presidents to convey our decision to their respective managers, and they to their employees. Simultaneously the decision was announced in our weekly newsletters. Pride goeth before a fall! Word of the decision spread rapidly, and even employees without cars were in an uproar.

I couldn't understand it. We had spent so much time discussing the issue, considering a wide range of possible options, ultimately reaching one seeming most fair. How could our judicious process have been met with widespread objection? I couldn't think of a better way to have approached the problem.

A few days later, an idea hit me. While top management had gone at it over five weeks of deliberation, perhaps we had also worked through the emotional impact of an action seeming contrary to the nurturing philosophy of our institution. After all Boston's Beth Israel Hospital was not a place that throws employees out of garages. Patients come first, of course, but we just don't do that sort of thing to employees!

Thinking about feelings as one confronts difficult issues reminded me of the stages of grief listed by Dr. Elizabeth Kübler-Ross,[18] a sequence of emotions noted among patients confronted with terminal illness — denial, anger, bargaining, depression, and acceptance. Had we worked through a similar cascade over five weeks of debate, taking time to reach emotional acceptance? Maybe so. But what did we then

[18] Kübler-Ross E. On Death and Dying: What the Dying Have to Teach Doctors. Nurses, Clergy and Their Own Families. 2014, Scribners, New York NY.

do? The vice-presidents announced to their department managers that top management has confronted the problem, and here is the solution. Now let's implement it. Done!

Not so fast. Even if practical aspects of a reasonable but discomfiting decision were grasped, did our middle managers do emotional work comparable to ours to reach their own acceptance? If managers at any level have not worked through accepting a difficult decision before they convey it to their employees, might that make it difficult for their subordinates to accept?

From this hypothesis, we reasoned that when the next tough issue surfaced, we would shape a communication process with timing by which both rational and emotional work could be done at each level, with feedback to the level above before going to the next lower step in the organization. We had no assurance of success, but the opportunity shortly arose to test it. Rising health care costs meant rising health insurance premiums for employees. We planned for the hospital's share of payment to rise, but so would that of employees. Recently in some industries, strikes had taken place as employees were told to pay more for their portion of the premium. Taking the time to provide step-wise for both the rational understanding and the emotional work that might help facilitate acceptance, we found that while no employee welcomed the increased financial burden, their understanding and acceptance were gained.

Our "Garage Caper" offered useful insight about communication. It makes sense that there are two components to greater acceptance of "bad news," the rational and the emotional. One must pay attention to both. We characterized this episode as a "Spectacular Failure," a well-intentioned action by management in response to a pressing need but one failing in its initial acceptance. It becomes "spectacular" upon leading to insight that can help the organization subsequently deal better with such necessary but onerous issues. Awareness of who may be affected by a proposed action and helping them work through to ultimate understanding and necessary acceptance should not be new to experienced managers. They would be correct to think we should have anticipated the response that surprised us.

SOME LESSONS LEARNED
A TOUGH MANAGER

Along with his excellence as a physician-scientist, my friend and colleague, Dr. Eugene Braunwald, is the best manager with whom I've ever worked. His mind is quick, and like a chess master, he sees moves and consequences well in advance, reaching conclusions often before the person presenting the issue may have finished. This can be frustrating; even getting the answer one seeks some feel he's difficult to deal with.

I valued working with him. His conclusions were data-based, rational, and dispassionate. Never irrevocably committed emotionally to a decision, he would always consider additional relevant information. He dealt with administrative matters as excellently as with clinical issues. Were one to emphasize relevant points not yet mentioned in matters whether administrative or clinical, he would consider the added information and reach a conclusion appropriate in light of the new facts. That he was called "tough" and difficult to deal with seemed to me ascribed by those unable to include everything they had planned to say, even though all the verbiage they may have thought necessary was not needed to reach a proper conclusion.

At meetings requested by others with me, I might find myself wondering what was their real issue of concern. Occasionally the question was answered as my visitor was about to exit, and with hand on the door, voiced, "Oh, by the way..." I elected to schedule occasional such sessions at the location of the requestor, which offered several advantages. Walking to and from their office, I could chat casually with others — it is important for the CEO to be seen informally more than rarely — and I could end the scheduled meeting more easily at my discretion.

Dallying in conversation reminded me of advice from then hospital counsel Gerald Gillerman, anticipating my first appearance at a deposition. "Just answer the question," he advised. "Telling the truth does not mean telling everything you know." Whether at a deposition or interacting elsewhere with others, gratification lies in conveying the relevant facts and reaching a proper conclusion, not in hearing one's self talk or trying to display how much one knows.

SOME LESSONS LEARNED
LETTERS OF PRAISE OR COMPLAINT

Not yet thirty-six when I entered the C-Suite (actually one office) at Beth Israel Hospital, I had some rough edges that needed sandpapering. Example: Replying to a nasty letter, the subject now forgotten, I wrote in longhand, then dictated and was about to sign a crisp defensive reply. At that moment, our board chair, Samuel L. Slosberg, a prince of a gentleman, happened to drop by. Pleased with its prickly content, I shared the correspondence. Reading through both letters, he paused, then looked at me.

"Mitch," he offered, "be right, but don't write." Many could probably author an essay, "A letter I shouldn't have written, or if written, shouldn't have sent." I was fortunate to get timely advice on this one.

Patients who complain to the hospital tend to remain willing to use the hospital. Those who air grievances elsewhere, sharing complaints with anyone who'll listen, give us little opportunity to know their issues and try to make things better. I recall the quality advantage Toyota early gained by encouraging and celebrating its employees to report not only errors in product quality but also what any worker deemed an "error in the making," the possibility that error in a production process might occur. We welcomed complaints, responded personally, meaningfully, and without delay. Tardy or standardized responses that appear emerging from "Drawer 3" put off people. Among the goals of any business beyond getting new customers is keeping the customers one already has.

We logged in complaints and immediately replied that "Your letter" is being looked into, and the writer (or caller) will get a meaningful reply once our investigation is completed. The log and follow-up were monitored in the effort not to delay our inquiry and response. The rare letter that suggested or threatened legal action led to immediate consultation with counsel and risk management.

A copy of most complaints was sent to the person most appropriate to offer direct perspective on the issue, along with a note from me, "Could you please give me some background on this matter?" I might walk over to a nursing station or other department to chat directly. From past experience, staff knew that my appearance would not be threatening. It is important there be no immediate implication of wrongdoing. Not only are there at least two sides to most stories, sometimes the patient or family may have misinterpreted an action or comment actually appropriate. (I remember a scene when, as chief resident in medicine at the Massachusetts General Hospital, in my stint in its Emergency Room I was advising a junior resident that a patient he had just seen needed overnight observation. The overnight ward was adjacent to the ER and the vernacular referring to it was "down back." I advised the resident, "Take her down back and sit on her." Unfortunately her husband missed the intention of my verbal shortcut and it took more than a bit of explanation before he calmed down.)

Often the employee's response gave enough information for our follow-up reply. If we've made a mistake, we say so, apologize, state what we can do about it, thank the individual for alerting us to the problem, and emphasize their communication will help us do better in the future. A phone call to the writer may be preferable, even an invitation to come in and see directly what we've done to remedy the matter. Years after such correspondence, I've come across patients or family members commenting how much they appreciated the prompt answer, that it came from the hospital CEO, and related directly to their voiced concern rather than being a late-arriving form letter offering nothing of substance.

When the complaint seems the result of misunderstanding, we try to clarify the issue. When it is found to be unjustified, we thank the writer for contacting us, adding that to learn how patients feel helps us improve our performance. That admits no wrong-doing, yet offers a gracious response.

Typically, a letter of complaint and final reply would be shared with all involved hospital staff. We wanted them to know how we responded to the writer. Copies would go into the patient's record, unless a specific staff member were named as offending. (In those days before the digital patient "chart," paper records made it easy to insert this correspondence.) Coming across that correspondence at a subsequent hospital visit, a physician or nurse might try to avoid the situation earlier complained of. With letters of praise, clinicians might want to emulate the previous favorable experience. Today, with the computerized patient record, the response can be done as before, but the letters may not as readily be incorporated. However, since BIDMC is a leader in real-time sharing of the medical record with patients and encouraging their input, complaints have a new way of being recorded and responded to.

With letters of praise, one reply suffices, thanking the writer for letting us know of their experience and reaction to it, adding that we'll share their comments with those involved, who we feel sure will be pleased their efforts have been so warmly received. Copies of both letter and reply go to staff named and their managers, and (previously) into the medical record. In the hallways or cafeteria or at the nursing station, coming across an employee so named I might add a compliment and thanks. They are pleased to know their managers and the CEO were aware of their good work.

From time to time, commendations are shared in our newsletters. Complaints, too, are published, for example, "I am eighty-three-years-old and of sound mind. I do not quite understand why a twenty-seven-year-old medical resident comes into my room and says, 'Good morning, Gertrude. I am Dr. Smith." Or, "I appreciated seeing signs in elevators about respecting patient privacy. But I was in an elevator and two doctors were talking about a patient. While they did not mention the patient's name, there was enough in the way of details that I, by chance, happened to recognize it was someone I knew who was currently in the hospital. I heard details that should not have been broadcast to me or anyone not involved in the care of that patient." Such letters both alert and caution staff and employees.

SOME LESSONS LEARNED

VIP

In a hospital, the designation "VIP" (Very Important Person) has two meanings. One relates to a "VIP Unit," where patients deemed "special" for one reason or another are given attention, accommodations, and services more personalized and elegant than the hospital's standard elsewhere. The VIP unit may offer luxury linen, more attractive menus, spacious comfortable arrangements for patient and visitors, afternoon tea and cookies in a common room complete with serenading pianist, and attendants eager to accommodate both needs and whims of the patients. I recall visiting a maternity unit where the arriving laboring mother-to-be was greeted with rose petals scattered on her bed, a harbinger of lush cosseting to follow. The second meaning refers to the patient given what some feel is a surfeit of overindulgence.

Having been asked several times to develop a VIP unit, we have not done so. Among the reasons, most relevant are:

1. Most patients today are hospitalized because they are very ill or their medical or surgical problem is complex. Such situations call for highly specialized expertise among both physicians and nurses and often very complex equipment. By contrast a VIP unit tends to gather patients for reasons other than specific clinical need. They present a gamut of medical and surgical issues,

and one cannot expect the VIP nursing staff to have comparable expertise in the happenstance range of disorders the patients may present. It is likely that their care will be less informed than on units where patients are grouped according to their illness, with nursing and medical staffs similarly congregated according to their specialized clinical expertise. On a VIP unit, imagine one patient recovering from serious trauma, another with burns, one post-cardiac transplant, another with a stroke, and one with bleeding esophageal varices. Regardless of the actual or assumed stature of the patient, it remains critical to deal with each patient by providing the very best specific medical and nursing resources available. So much hospital care today is technologically individualized such that no VIP unit staff could be expected to have mastered the wide range of technology and care for a mix of sick patients. As a result, a VIP unit may tend to become populated with privileged individuals whose illness may be mild, even not requiring hospitalization. Assigned to such units, and pressured more on providing creature comfort than dealing with complex therapeutic issues, many skilled and competent nurses become disenchanted.

2. A VIP Unit could suggest to patients and hospital employees that patient care and attention elsewhere in the hospital may be lower in quality or attention than what is provided in the VIP Unit.

Patients tend to be given the VIP designation because of title or position in life, or thought to have the potential or actuality of being a major donor to the hospital. Over decades medical history is replete with stories of clinical disasters where VIP patients received "special treatment" to their disadvantage or even death. Examples might be the clinician's failure to do a rectal exam to avoid the patient's assumed discomfort, only to miss a rectal cancer that ultimately kills, or agreeing to the patient's insistence that surgery be done by the world-famous but aging surgeon who has not been in the OR for years.

Every patient should be treated as "special,'" with competent personalized attention of the highest quality. Indicated essential diagnostic and therapeutic measures must not be bypassed for social considerations. I recall an instance where only a week after her admission, I became aware of a patient from a very wealthy family. Going to the medically appropriate floor, with standard accommodations, I asked the nurse manager about visiting the patient, adding my surprise not to have been aware earlier of her admission. She replied that the patient had been admitted in her seventh month because of a threatened pregnancy and was to be at strict bed rest with no unnecessary interruptions. That admission was held in confidence from our development office and from me. It was the right thing to do, I agreed, and went back to my office without seeing the patient.

Much later after her successful delivery, the patient dropped by my office to compliment the staff on her care. Congratulating her on the outcome, I related the story of my intention to visit her in the hospital and being turned away by the nurses, emphasizing it was proper care in her interest for nursing to insist that she not be disturbed. By contrast the patient recalled that several years previously at another hospital, she entered her room in its VIP unit only to find the hospital CEO already there. "... fluffing the pillows!"

SOME LESSONS LEARNED
MERGERS AND ORGANIZATIONAL KNOWLEDGE

Toward the close of my time as CEO at Beth Israel Hospital, we and New England Deaconess, a neighboring Harvard-affiliated teaching hospital, planned to merge. With few exceptions, there was broad agreement. Some observers predicted more dissent than actually arose. The most prominent issue surfaced trying to merge the two departments of anesthesiology. At BI, its financial arrangement was typical of academic institutions: physicians' fees went into a pool controlled by the respective department chairs. (In hospitals owned by a medical school, often it is the dean who controls this income.) The fees for service paid to physicians in academia are used not only for salaries, benefits, and direct costs of those who generate the income but also for example toward department overhead costs, salary support for other department staff, academic support for new recruits, teaching, and research efforts, etc. By contrast, Deaconess was well-served by a separate and private group of very competent anesthesiologists also providing care at several other hospitals. They divided revenues among their own salaries, benefits, and other operating costs, but not having the academic responsibilities of the BI department, were able to provide higher take-home salaries than we could offer. In the merged department, it would not have been possible to have two anesthesiologists of comparable length of service and academic status provide comparable service under significantly different salaries. Early discussions led to tension; I should have handled the issue better, though outcome might have been little different. The Deaconess group elected to leave but continued to function responsibly until we could add several more clinicians to bring the merged department up to its needed complement. No patient suffered as a result.

Several books on mergers point out that one measure of success, taken five to seven years post-merger, is whether the new organization has gone successfully from "we-they" to "us." That is what actually took place at Beth Israel Deaconess Medical Center.

Success was fostered in large part through moves functionally integrating the two institutions, which are sited diagonally opposite across Brookline and Longwood Avenues close to Harvard Medical School. (I had proposed an elevated crossway to connect the two campuses, not savoring staff crossing the busy intersection, especially late at night or in foul weather, but the Boston Redevelopment Authority denied our request, commenting, "It would destroy the cityscape.") At time of merger, the Emergency Unit at BI (which became the "East Campus") had reached capacity. Because enlarging it was not feasible, a new location was sought without favoring any site in advance. What made best sense turned out to be an area at Deaconess ("West Campus"). Logically following the new construction (exceptionally well designed under the insightful eye of Emergency Medicine Chief Dr. Richard Wolff) were moves from East to West of the rooftop helicopter pad, surgical and medical ICUs, cardiac surgery, and cardiology. Remaining on the East Campus included obstetrics, general medical and surgery floors, ambulatory surgery, a major endoscopy unit, and most ambulatory care. It would have been difficult to argue the West Campus had been poorly treated in the merger.

Equally important than even-handedness with regard to facilities was consideration of the frustrations and other feelings of employees and staff, initially at the prospect of merger and then over the months following. Few mergers seem not heralded with declarations of "cultural compatibility," but smooth integration calls for more than such pronouncements. Mergers can be traumatic at all levels of the organization. Anxiety goes beyond anticipated threat of job loss; it can persist well after whatever rearrangements or downsizing have taken place. Long-lasting discomfort may arise through disruptions in organizational knowledge.

Organizational knowledge can be explicit or tacit. With merger in the offing, organization leadership carries out "due diligence," examining each other. Typically the inquiry relates to explicit details of the business itself, future prospects, and related financial aspects. But cultural "due diligence" is rarely done to a comparable extent, examining the way each organization functions, shaped by its particular history, and how words, phrases, attitudes seeming identical in both actually may differ in their respective meanings and operational realities. Without each party's insight into the way the other really works, rude surprises can lie ahead.

In their book, *Working Knowledge*, authors Thomas H. Davenport and Laurence Prusak[19] explore the nature of internal organizational

[19] Davenport TH, Prusak L. Working Knowledge: How Organizations Manage What They Know. Brighton, Massachusetts. Harvard Business School Press, 1988.

knowledge. It may be explicit — in documents, written policies, and other artifacts, but another component is tacit, unstated but existing in the minds of various individuals — ways to get things done, whom to contact to find out something needed or useful, what informal network can facilitate a desired action, whom to trust. Each organization has its rich store of tacit knowledge. Over time employees acquire tacit knowledge, enabling them to navigate more comfortably and effectively day-to-day as they learn how to accomplish the company's goals and their own.

What happens to tacit knowledge in a merger? With loss of tacit knowledge held by employees let go, voids are created. And some of tacit knowledge retained will lose validity as organizational arrangements change. Among those remaining in the merged organization, many will work under new managers. Others will acquire new subordinates. Few may have the comfort of knowing or doing things in ways that existed at their pre-merger company. Some may feel disoriented as their new department, revamped by merger, strives to regain smooth operation. Employees must work to get to know both their own new operation and what goes on elsewhere and how to use that new awareness productively. It can be frustrating to figure out who really knows what one needs to find out, or how to get done those things that, pre-merger, seemed readily accomplished by a quick phone call, e-mail, corridor chat, or lunchtime contact with the "right person" whom one knew and trusted.

In a stable organization, orientation of new employees entering from time to time begins their acquisition of explicit institutional knowledge appropriate to effective functioning. Over time they come to understand the informal networks and pathways. In a merger, many employees become "new" because the organization is new; they can't "go home" again. The new working culture takes time to jell and even longer to forge organization-wide knowledge. The "cultural compatibility" voiced pre-merger may have related more to mission, perhaps leadership style or human resource policy. The comfort of employees prior to merger had derived from their unique body of specific institutional knowledge, explicit and tacit, accrued over time within each organization. Individualized informal knowledge store of how to know and how to do was grease that made the machinery work more or less smoothly. With mergers much of that can vanish. A discomfiting loss, it has to be rebuilt over time. These inevitable changes in work culture often seem ignored.

Merger calls for appreciation of the day-to-day working knowledge inherent in each organization and the sea-changes that follow merger. Awareness of the need to forge new ways to do and to know becomes important in facilitating the transition from "we-they" to "us." Communication of change becomes critical. There should be clear and frequent descriptions — new departments, who heads them, where located, their functions and accountability, how and when to reach them, etc. Equally important are seemingly social encounters — receptions, teas, coffees, other informal gatherings — where people from one side get to meet and know those from the other, helping avoid the disadvantage of employees dealing with disembodied names and voices on their phones, computers, and in written interactions. Mentoring roles can be useful, probing to learn where people feel stymied in effectively doing their work and finding ways to illuminate developing organizational knowledge, explicit and tacit. Such efforts could strengthen "cultural compatibility," a concept that must include helping the work force comprehend and ultimately navigate the merged organization as positively as they have the old.

CHAPTER 6: COMPETITIVE ADVANTAGE

BEYOND "QUALITY OF CARE"

One of the many ways in which Boston is unique is its many excellent hospitals and medical schools. In the city proper (population about 700,000), most hospitals are medical school affiliated, teaching and training medical, nursing, and other health care students and graduates of Harvard, Boston University, Tufts, Massachusetts Institute of Technology, Northeastern University, Simmons, and other schools throughout Boston, the US, and abroad. Prominent in biomedical research, each Boston teaching hospital has strong capability in almost every clinical specialty and subspecialty. The quality of medical care in Boston is very good, but none of its prestigious institutions can gain advantage through claim of expertise invariably outshining that of others. In such a competitive environment, how can one hospital distinguish itself? Some attempt by building image as a leading research institution, but even there none has dominance, only varying in focus or size rather than quality of expertise in its research effort.

Our own intention is to provide warm, personalized patient care of the highest quality, informed by research and teaching. It is directed by two questions, (1) How can we help the patient? and (2) In doing so, what can we learn? These are important but not unique. More was needed to forge a competitive advantage for Boston's Beth Israel Hospital. "Competitive advantage" is not defined by better pricing, lower costs, growing admissions, or a better bottom line — these may be some of the results. It lies in making the hospital surpassingly attractive to people seeking or thinking about health care. Competitive advantage comes from (1) establishing a welcoming, reassuring, responsive, and effective clinical environment for patients; (2) creating an efficient, comfortable, and personally fulfilling workplace for physicians, nurses, other employees, and volunteers; and (3) being deservedly recognized as helpful and devoted to health and well-being in the eyes of the community we serve.

The following efforts are samples of what has been achieved at BI. They should be understood as products of their time. For any institution, opportunities arise continuously, calling for constant alertness and creativity. Before my tenure at Beth Israel Hospital, Dr. Paul M. Zoll triggered the field of electrocardiology with his pioneering work on cardiac pacemakers and defibrillation. Dr. Herrman L. Blumgart opened the field of non-invasive study of cardiac function by measuring the time of passage of a radioactive compound from its injection in one arm to detection in the other. On the administrative side, our home care program was the first in Boston. Even earlier at its start in 1916, Beth Israel Hospital offered a comforting environment to Eastern European Jews newly arrived to a strange new environment, and later an opportunity for hospital training and practice to newly-minted physicians emerging from that same culture of immigrants. Physicians from an earlier wave, largely from Germany and Austria, had already begun to make their way in Boston's medical schools and teaching hospitals, and they took part in forging pathways for the new immigrants, along with other considerate members of the established medical community.

Following my tenure, which ended after the merger of BI with New England Deaconess Hospital, an impressive system of care has been created under CEO Dr. Kevin Tabb, initially including several community hospitals, adding walk-in centers and other caregiving facilities, and most recently connecting with another large group, Lahey Health, creating an organized system affording patients throughout Greater Boston ready access to our care and their own medical record. Among the characteristics differentiating this BI-Lahey system are that the hospitals and physicians work together negotiating with third-party payers, in contrast to the more common situation where the two parties may tend to vie with each other for relative advantage in such negotiations. And as Dr. Tabb became increasingly focused on corporate issues, the personal intimacy of what was BI, now Beth Israel Deaconess Medical Center, has been strengthened once again by its current excellent CEO, Peter Healy.

Innovations do not need to be unique; they must serve a purpose timely, advantageous to the innovating organization, its customers or staff. That creates competitive advantage. The key is to identify such needs, ideally before others do or create a better approach than currently exists. Even something whimsical can turn out to be helpful. Some years ago, our chef created his own recipe for chocolate chip cookies, and before long, in the annual "Best of Boston" listing in Boston Magazine under "Best Chocolate Chip Cookies," we were surprised to take first prize. These cookies remain available on occasion in our hospital cafeterias as good as ever.

This chapter offers creative examples from my tenure that have helped differentiate BI from other hospitals, each designed the better to help meet needs of one set or more of our various "customers." None denigrates other institutions. To the extent these benefit our patients, physicians, other scientists, nurses, medical students, employees at all levels, our Board, Harvard Medical School, the world-wide collection of knowledge and capability in medicine and health care, or the general community, coming from Beth Israel Hospital they helped strengthen our competitive advantage.

COMPETITIVE ADVANTAGE
EXCELLENCE IN RESEARCH

Outstanding research tends to attract other MD's and PhD's. Dr. Harold F. Dvorak, then chair of pathology at BI, discovered that tumor cells secrete a growth factor stimulating blood vessel formation, without which tumors cannot grow. His critical finding led to ways of counteracting the action of this vascular endothelial growth factor (VEGF) and several other similar factors he later identified. Medication to impair their actions (anti-VEGF) has proven useful in treatment of several cancers and also beneficial for treating "wet macular degeneration." For his scientific achievements, Dr. Dvorak has received many prestigious awards, the most notable being the Canada Gairdner International Award 2014, commonly viewed as a pathway to the Nobel Prize.

In his time at Beth Israel, Dr. Lewis Cantley elucidated the enzyme, PI 3-kinase, determining it to be of major importance in the understanding of cancer. Named phosphoinositide 3-kinase, it is one of a family of enzymes involved in cell growth, differentiation and angiogenesis (blood vessel formation). Critical for the growth of cancers, it also has impact in diabetes. Recipient of many prestigious awards, Dr. Cantley has also been cited as a candidate worthy of the Nobel Prize.

Several years ago, Dr. Cantley moved from Boston's Beth Israel to the Meyer Cancer Center of Weill Cornell Medical College in New York City, where he continues to investigate and develop promising molecular approaches to therapy. We were both saddened and proud upon Dr. Cantley's move to Cornell. My view is that if none of our faculty is ever recruited to a position offering greater opportunity in another institution of excellence or potential thereof (larger lab space with greater resources for investigation, major academic promotion such as a department chairmanship, deanship, etc., or of late, a challenging role in industry), we are not doing our job of helping nurture their growth in scholarship and capability.

With their impressive achievements while under our roof, Dr. Dvorak, Dr. Cantley, and other research and clinical scholars add to our institution's current prestige and its attractiveness to the upcoming generation of biomedical scholars, clinicians, and teachers of outstanding growth potential, thus helping enhance further the quality of scholarship and care in our own academic medical center.

COMPETITIVE AVANTAGE
PRIMARY NURSING

Competitive advantage is gained through the way patients respond to their hospital experience, beyond feeling their clinical care was technically first-rate. At BI a major advance in professional nursing care came with the 1972 recruitment of Joyce C. Clifford, RN, MSN. PhD, Vice President for Nursing. She instituted Primary Nursing, a concept creatively put forth by Marie Manthey, RN, BSN, MSN, nurse executive at the University of Minnesota Medical Center.[20] Manthey's insight revolutionized hospital practice of nursing.

Nearly a century ago, the head nurse typically was located at a central desk in an open ward of some sixteen or more patients. Sharing her clinical observations and insights with the resident physicians manning the ward, she led and acted directly in the care of all the patients assisted by other nurses on the unit. As open wards became eliminated and single and double rooms the mode, "Team Nursing" emerged, ostensibly to improve efficiency by having each nurse focus on specific tasks for all patients rather than provide full care for a few. With Team Nursing, one nurse might take the vital signs (blood pressure, pulse rate, respiratory rate, temperature) of every patient in the unit. Another would dispense medications to all. A third might change linens or give bed baths. Tasks such as cleaning the incontinent patient, often called "scut work," were designated to nursing aides or orderlies. With that fragmentation, no nurse might know enough to convey a full picture of any

[20] Manthey M, Ciske K, Robertson P, Harris I. Primary Nursing: A return to the concept of "my nurse" and "my patient." Nursing Forum 9(1);65-84:1970A.

one patient's illness or progress, how well the patient understood the illness, anticipated ability to care for self once discharged, or how the demands of care might affect family members.

Under Team Nursing, because nurses often learned less than possible about any one patient and his or her daily needs and progress, the patient might feel less secure, less informed, and less cared for. Status of the nurse suffered in relationship with both physician and patient. Time spent by the professional nurse in simple acts of patient contact — bed baths, skin care, bedpans, and others more mundane were often declared wasteful of the nurse's intellect and training, no longer appreciated as time critical in helping piece together the multitude of observations available of the patient's clinical status, time for the nurse to forge fragmented data into a meaningful whole to be shared with the patient's physician and applied professionally to the care of the patient. How better could one make nurses feel powerless, how better to denigrate their training and experience?

Joyce Clifford, Vice-President for Nursing, brought a groundbreaking change to Beth Israel. She understood Manthey's concept of Primary Nursing. (Note: It is "Primary Nursing," not "primary care nursing.") Primary Nursing affirmed that nurses are professionals, educated in medical and nursing care, and like physicians, grow in expert clinical judgment with relevant experience. Consistent with their education, training, experience and expertise, nurses should have requisite authority to register and act upon her or his judgments within the context of the patients' health care needs and the collegial relationships with patients' physicians.

Primary Nursing at Beth Israel Hospital[21] assigned a specific nurse to develop nursing care plans for each of five or six patients, in conjunction with their physicians' medical care plans. Working at the bedside, the Primary Nurse would care directly for those patients, carrying out her plans. Others, nurses and aides, would work with the

---

[21] Clifford JC. Primary Nursing. A contemporary model for delivery of care. Am J Health Syst Pharm. 1980;37:1098-1109.

Primary Nurse under her or his direction. At the next shift, the nurse coming on duty would learn what the Primary Nurse's care plans were for each of those patients and the progress of each over the past eight hours or so, follow the guidelines set by the Primary Nurse, work her own shift at the bedside, modifying care appropriately should the patients' clinical needs change. The same would hold true for the next shift. Next morning when the Primary Nurse returned, the departing third shift nurse would convey what had taken place over the past sixteen hours. Then as physician and Primary Nurse made morning rounds, the Primary Nurse would report full details of the patients' progress over the past twenty-four hours. Together Primary Nurse and physician would plan for the next twenty-four hours of care, each well-informed by the other.

Beyond clinical judgments on the patient's status, the Primary Nurse made other decisions. These could be administrative, such as rescheduling timing of an early morning x-ray once that department summoned, because the patient was still waiting for breakfast, the latter delayed until blood for fasting chemistries had been drawn.

The role change in Primary Nursing was new to most of our physicians. Some immediately saw its virtue; others hesitated because a physician might now have to seek out more than one Primary Nurse for his or her several patients. Each separate briefing took more physician time than in the past when the desk-bound head nurse reported more limited information from a Cardex, but each primary nurse's update gave more complete information that improved efficiency and effectiveness of the physician's encounter with patients. Joyce Clifford had the backing of administration. Together we had discussed the move to Primary Nursing with several chiefs of service but not proposing it as an "experiment" where, should physicians object, we would go back to the old ways. Believing this was a move for better care, we offered to see how things would be in three to six months, expecting by then that Primary Nursing would have convinced most. And it did.

Making major organizational change calls for a thoughtful approach, Dr. Clifford introduced the concept of Primary Nursing to her nurse managers (previously called head nurses), and through them, the entire nursing staff. Sensing who among her staff seemed more receptive, she began with the most enthusiastic nurse manager and her unit. With success on the first and then another, nursing units were converted one by one until Primary Nursing flourished throughout the hospital. Nationally it was a first-of-its-kind achievement.

Critics elsewhere argued that Primary Nursing would be more expensive, but our nursing hours per patient remained unchanged, falling in the middle among those of Boston's major teaching hospitals. True, more nursing time was spent at the bedside, but nursing supervisors disappeared along with other administrative nurses no longer needed since decision-making and interaction with physicians were now in the hands of the bedside nurses. Some technical improvements helped as well. For example, a computerized dispensing system for narcotics that controlled and documented usage eliminated the time-honored need for that critical senior nurse roaming the hospital who had what I called "the keys to the liquor cabinet."

The impact went beyond quality of care and the status of nursing. Recruiting reshaped the staff almost exclusively to nurses with bachelor's degrees or higher. BI became a preferred place to work. At a time of nursing shortage in Boston where at another hospital the nursing complement on an individual unit on any day might have been only nurses from an agency, that is without any of the hospital's own staff nurses, at BI only rarely did we have to "float" nurses from one unit to patch up a transient shortage on another.

Encouraged by the delegation of accountability and responsibility, many nurses went on to get advanced degrees. Unlike practice common elsewhere, where a master's or doctor's degree meant that the nurse would likely depart from bedside care to become a supervisor or other administrator, our nurses brought their advanced education directly to the bedside and the patient. Because nurses enter the profession to care for patients, continuing at the bedside was reinforced through creation of a ladder for clinical nursing. Responding to the stages of professional development lucidly delineated by Patricia Benner, RN, PhD in "From Novice to Expert,"[22] Dr. Clifford instituted "Levels of Practice," with strict criteria applied to experience, capability and performance of bedside nurses. With each recognized advance to a higher designated level of practice, nurses gained in both stature and income, achieving added responsibility for teaching and mentoring younger nurses while remaining a valued Primary Nurse practicing at the bedside. Most physicians gain in knowledge, stature, and income, yet remain in direct patient care; why not the same for nurses? Some advanced bedside nurses were also designated as consultants, available to help a nurse on another unit in management of a patient whose illness related to the specialized expertise of the consultant. And when academic presentations were to be given at national or international meetings, one of the bedside nurses involved in the study to be reported might take the podium, rather than one from a higher management echelon.

The nature of salary for nurses changed. We abandoned the conventional nursing practice of hourly wage, with X cents per hour more for nights and Y for weekends and holidays. Nurses were paid salaries as are other professionals. A base salary was adjusted for the extent of nights and weekends planned for each nurse. What followed was disappearance of the notion of working overtime. Nurses left each shift when they finished what they intended to do, sometimes one, two, or more hours beyond the conventional shift change time. Recognized as carrying out their professional responsibilities in the interests of their patients, they were not simply "putting in" eight hours.

Primary Nursing developed at Beth Israel was not implemented intact upon our merger with New England Deaconess Hospital. While it was working smoothly at BI, one could not simply switch overnight

22 Benner, Patricia. From Novice to Expert: Excellence and Power in Clinical Nursing Practice. 1984. Addison-Wesley Publication Company, Menlo Park, CA.

the nursing program on the West Campus to primary nursing. BI nurses were moved to units appropriate to their expertise, and these became scattered throughout both the East and West campus. What emerged was a modification that retains the primacy of bedside professional nursing and the working professional colleagueship with the physician. A graphic illustration of that colleagueship is seen in the *cinéma vérité* by Frederick Wiseman, "Near Death."[23] It was filmed at our BI Medical ICU long after formal professional dress codes for nurses or physicians disappeared. Most observers would be unable to tell not only from clothing but from their interaction with each other who in the film was a nurse and who a physician; they were indistinguishable as co-equal clinicians.

With so many more career opportunities open to women today, a potential future shortage of nurses may be too little appreciated and one of its possible causes too little understood. To the extent a well-educated nurse is deprived of the opportunity to function as a professional or denied recognition as such, with loss of appropriate authority and autonomy, it is understandable that fewer women or men may choose this profession. Working to counteract that issue is both Primary Nursing and the growing professional autonomy of the nurse practitioner.

Several years after Primary Nursing began at Beth Israel, I had a thought about my unhesitating resonance with the concept. When I was a house officer at the Massachusetts General Hospital in the mid-fifties, much of my training experience took place on open wards of sixteen to eighteen beds. Two desks faced each other in the center of the ward, one for the head nurse, the other for the second-year resident in charge. Internal medicine was more slowly paced then. It was not uncommon, for example, to decide that a patient with pneumonia, now afebrile and much better, might be kept on medication and discharged several days later once we were fully satisfied with complete resolution

---

[23] The title, "Near Death," referred not to the fact that a few MICU patients died but that the staff were constantly working so close to potential mortality.

of the chest x-ray findings. With that pace and the slow turnover it accommodated, it was not difficult for the head nurse to know and lead in the actual delivery of care to all patients on the ward, more readily knowing virtually everything of clinical importance about each of them, sharing in the physician's diagnostic impressions and plans for the work-up and treatment. The head nurse would develop and carry out her nursing care plan, know the day-to-day evolution of each patient's status, the state of their psyches, readiness for self or family care at home, etc., in short, all aspects that fall within the proper realm of knowledge and awareness for the professional nurse who carries primary responsibility for the patient.

Knowing all that about their patients, the head nurse on those wards was truly a professional colleague in their care, many times often more knowledgeable and more capable than my house officer colleagues and me. While it was my role and responsibility as intern or resident to write "orders," I knew it was the knowledge, awareness, and professional judgment of the ward's head nurse that enabled me to shape the appropriateness of the orders I "wrote" and she "followed." The professional colleagueship on those wards was the essence of Primary Nursing, but at the time the insight to identify it as such was missing.

Primary Nursing at Beth Israel restored the nurse to her or his important role, that of fundamental professional in the hospital care of patients. Nurses provide the continuous nurture and 24/7 observation and care, evaluating, supporting, and sustaining the patient for the physician's episodic observations and interventions. Equally critical is that nurses maintain the continuous informed observation that monitors progress of illness, the impact of interventions and happenstance occurrences, and they gain insight into the patient's (and family's) capacity to manage the illness and recovery post-discharge.

With today's pace on inpatient floors, the Primary Nurse's accountability for five or six patients is a challenge similar to that of several times as many patients when I was a medical resident. Today's Primary

Nurse is placed squarely with her or his patients, enjoys hands-on direct contact paralleling that of the past in the open ward. Sadly, the virtues of ward nursing, appreciated and even savored by interns, residents, and nurses more than half a century ago, were not extended as the wards disappeared. It took nearly three-quarters of a century for Marie Manthey at the University of Minnesota to articulate the concept and for Joyce Clifford at Boston's Beth Israel Hospital to implement Primary Nursing hospital-wide.

COMPETITIVE ADVANTAGE
SHARING THE MEDICAL RECORD

Interest growing nationally in sharing the medical record with the patient began in the medical clinic of Dr. Thomas L. Delbanco, a creative internist on the Beth Israel staff. In his work-up of a new patient, he asked about alcohol history. Getting a casual denial of anything more than rare, minimal, social consumption but doubting its veracity from one patient's appearance and overall history, he jotted "? Alcohol" in his notes. Later in the interview, realizing that his patient, whose occupation included setting up type for text to be printed, was glancing at his, to the patient, upside down notes, Dr. Delbanco took an imaginative approach.

"I know you can easily read my notes upside down. What about where I raised the question of more alcohol consumption than you just admitted?"

After a long pause, the patient replied, "Yeah, Doc, you got it right."

Sharing the written medical record, that time by happenstance, brought to the fore a new subject of meaning to the patient's health, enabling it to be talked about openly, shared together by doctor and patient, offering information and therapeutic opportunities otherwise possibly unavailable. From that one prescient encounter, Dr. Delbanco went on to institutionalize sharing the medical record with patients, first at BI and later more widely. Subsequently, he expanded patients' involvement by enabling them to enter not only corrections (They may not be infrequent, "It was a fractured femur, not hip," or "It was hepatitis B, not A.") but also comments that at times might embellish the content already in the record or, at others, illuminate attitudes of the patient worth awareness of clinicians providing the patient's care. Sharing the medical record has proven of value locally and is generating growing interest and use elsewhere.

COMPETITIVE ADVANTAGE
THE RIGHTS OF PATIENTS

In 1972 I became aware of a statement on patients' rights issued by a clinic in Cleveland, the Hough Norwood Family Health Center. A comparable assurance seemed appropriate for Beth Israel Hospital. Working with colleagues and hospital counsel, we issued the very first for hospital patients. Over the years, the statement has little changed; its basic message remains intact. The first edition was introduced to our employees, medical staff, and the public in August 1972.

In the hospital's Employee Newsletter and our Dear Dr. Newsletter, I wrote, "The text will serve as a gentle reminder to us of the stature, humanity, and importance of our patients. About thirty persons from all segments of our Hospital community have helped in the editing... It states simply some of the facts of which patients should be aware as they seek our help. Your comments are invited."

Titled, "Your Rights as a Patient at Beth Israel Hospital, Boston, Massachusetts," our statement opened:

> Beth Israel Hospital, its doctors, nurses, and entire staff are committed to assure you excellent care as our patient. It has always been our policy to respect your individuality and your dignity. This listing is published to be certain that you know of the long-standing rights that are yours as a Beth Israel patient.

Its closing:

> Beth Israel Hospital is interested in keeping you in the best health possible. If you feel you are not being treated fairly or properly, you have the right to discuss this with your doctor, nurse, unit manager, other health worker, or the Administrator-on-Call. You may also write a letter to the General Director, Beth Israel Hospital, Boston, Massachusetts 02215. All correspondence will receive prompt and personal attention.
>
> This message reflects the interest and philosophy of the entire staff of Beth Israel Hospital.

Now widely posted (with slight variations) in virtually every US hospital and many abroad, our statement was intended to educate patients on positive expectations for attention, excellent medical care, respect, privacy, candid sharing with them of information about their care and treatment, knowing who was providing their care, access to their medical record, right to leave the hospital, freedom to ask questions or complain without any diminution in our attention or care.

The statement also listed responsibilities we felt patients should take: keep appointments or notify the hospital when one cannot do so, be respectful and considerate of other patients, be prompt in payments due. We emphasized that should a patient perceive a problem in his or her care, he or she should feel free to let us know about it and understand that we will not take amiss their raising a problem but do all we reasonably can to resolve the issue.

Following our August 1972 publication of "Your Rights as a Patient at Beth Israel Hospital, Boston," the Commission on Medical Malpractice appointed by the Secretary of HEW (now HHS) reprinted both our statement and that of the Hough Norwood Family Health Center, commenting, "The Commission believes that these statements set forth the minimum rights that should be accorded all patients."[24] In December 1972, the American Hospital Association published and disseminated nationally its version, titled, "Statement on a Patient's Bill of Rights."

COMPETITIVE ADVANTAGE
ORDERS NOT TO RESUSCITATE

In the early seventies, I came across a young nurse clenching her fists and weeping at the door of a patient's room.

She sputtered, "Why can't they let him alone?" Inside the room, an elderly patient, consumed with widespread metastatic prostate cancer, had died — his heart had stopped. Having had all treatment possible in past months, he had been admitted with terminal illness, a situation not unusual at that time before hospice care was more common. Nothing more could be done beyond pain relief, hydration, and what possible comfort might be provided until his inevitable death. But at that moment, a resident physician was applying CPR, external cardiopulmonary resuscitation. With each thrust on his chest, it seemed another cancer-devoured rib had cracked. This was an abuse of the patient, I stated, by no means offering any help or comfort. The effort stopped.

At that time, virtually no hospital seemed to offer clear policy or protocol for instituting CPR. Initially found helpful for the rare surgical patient suffering cardiac arrest secondary to anesthesia administration, CPR use then spread to actual and some presumed cardiac arrests throughout hospitals and ultimately elsewhere. The initial wider and generally uncontrolled use of CPR brought about a series of hospital problems, including:

- With no standard protocol, decisions often fell to an intern or resident and varied widely in terms of why and when use of CPR was felt to be appropriate.

[24] United States Department of Health, Education, and Welfare. Report of the Secretary's Commission on Medical Malpractice (Publication No[OS] 73-88. Washington, DC. January 16, 1973.

- Some physicians worried over possibility of a lawsuit if they did not use CPR, even when they knew it to be useless. Others were concerned that family members would feel the physician did not do enough for the patient.
- Even knowing when CPR was pointless, physicians might feel that "something should be done" to reassure family. The absence of policy led to half-hearted efforts, such as "bag breathe but don't intubate," or "walk, but don't run for help to the phone." In some hospitals, a dot of specific color was pasted on the medical chart, indicating the nature of a "try," should the patient arrest.
- The issue of patients' wishes was largely untouched, even though universally understood was that a sentient patient can refuse treatment of any kind, with few exceptions.
- Dilemmas existed on who made decisions for the patient unable to make his or her own wishes known or how to deal with a possible division of opinion among family members.

In 1974 the American Medical Association proposed that decisions not to resuscitate be formally entered into the patient's medical record and communicated to all relevant staff. Little policy or action followed. In 1976 several Harvard clinicians and others discussed the need for clarification and standardization of policy, to replace the current spectrum of *ad hoc* decision-making. We felt several things should emerge, particularly:

- Which patient might benefit from CPR, which not; how to decide and whom to inform.
- How to invite, discuss, and respond to statements from the patient about his or her care in the anticipated event of cessation of vital functions.
- Who should act for the non-sentient patient.
- How to deal with pressures or other considerations put forth by the patient's family or others should they differ from the sentient patient's prior wishes.

In August 1976, a seminal article from Beth Israel Hospital was published in the New England Journal of Medicine, "Orders Not to Resuscitate."[25] Two others were included, one from the Massachusetts General Hospital, the other from philosopher and ethicist Sissela Bok, PhD. The first of those two referred in general terms to situations where cessation of therapeutic measures may be indicated, the need for consensus (not necessarily absolute) among those relevant and sharing in the care of the patient, and the importance of informing the family. Nothing was stated about prior decisions or requests from a sentient patient. Sissela Bok proposed a "Living Will" statement, ideally made previously by a sentient patient, one that should prevail unless unlawful. She also argued that a proxy be designated within that Living Will, an individual specifically named previously by the sentient patient to make choices about treatment were that patient no longer able to do so. And that the patient should be kept informed about his or her status, including likelihood of CPR.

Authored by two hospital attorneys and me, our statement was developed through discussion with many individuals at BI, physicians, nurses, social workers. We emphasized first that the policy of the hospital is to act affirmatively to preserve the life of all patients and added that our policy also included respecting the competent patient's informed acceptance or rejection of treatment, including cardiopulmonary resuscitation.

I felt there were two specific situations where a new policy should apply, one less common, the other more so:

- A competent patient who is not deemed irreversibly and irreparably ill issues instructions that under stated circumstances, he or she approves of or opposes the use of certain procedures (An example might be a patient with lung cancer and metastases on

[25] Rabkin MT, Gillerman G, Rice NR. Orders Not To Resuscitate. N Engl J Med 1976;295:364-366.

the pericardium, the sac surrounding the heart. A terminal arrhythmia might result with cardiac arrest.) Here the physician must explore with the patient the clinical meaning of anticipated possible situations and their likelihood and consequences, including possibility of death. Should the properly informed and sentient patient make a decision, the physician and the institution are obliged to carry out the patient's instructions.

- Where the patient is irreversibly and irreparably ill and death is imminent — in the article we postulated about two weeks or so — consideration of appropriateness of resuscitation is warranted in advance of possible cessation of vital functions, if not already raised by the patient. The patient's situation is evaluated through thoughtful medical judgment by the responsible clinician or clinicians, in consultation with other physicians attending on the patient, relevant nursing and other staff active in the care of the patient, plus at least one other senior staff physician not previously involved in that patient's care. The question is, "…whether the patient's death is so certain and so imminent that resuscitation in the event of sudden cessation of vital functions would serve no purpose." In that case, the team concludes to let nature take its course but continues with no diminution of actions for comfort, pain relief, hydration, and nutrition as appropriate. One must not feel guilty for that decision, even in the face of family pressure.

We emphasized that the writing and performance of Orders Not to Resuscitate become effective only:

- Upon informed choice of the competent patient. It cannot be overruled.
- With an incompetent patient, to the extent that all family members (e.g., those who would sign a *post mortem* autopsy permission) agree with the recommendation of involved hospital staff. Unlike Dr. Bok, we did not consider the role of a des-

ignated proxy, a concept only emerging at the time. Today the proxy designated previously by the sentient patient, whether family member(s) or other(s) would be decision-maker(s) for the now incompetent patient.

- Emphasis on sharing information among all relevant caregivers on any decision thus made on what to do, daily review of the patient's situation, and the right of the competent patient to change his or her mind at any time.
- Regardless of whatever decision is extant, emphasis that there is to be no decrease in appropriate medical and nursing attention and care.

A recent review of developments over the decades since added the comment, "By providing a formal framework for the decision-making process and the communication of these decisions, DNR (Do Not Resuscitate) policies filled a void at health care institutions. Medical staff could now discuss DNR decisions with the patient or family well before they were likely to be needed. Equally important, the upshot of these discussions could then be communicated in a standard fashion to potential responders in cross-covering shifts, many of whom might have only limited knowledge of a patient's case but who could now feel more confident about the integrity of the decision."[26]

COMPETITIVE ADVANTAGE
THE SCANLON PLAN

In the mid-1980's, as pressures mounted for greater efficiency and cost-saving, we discussed ways to strengthen employee and staff commitment to the hospital's mission. Laura Avakian, Vice President, Human Resources, began to explore programs in participative management. With her staff member, Emanuel Berger, they became interested in The Scanlon Plan. Its enthusiastic proponents in industry seemed led

[26] Burns JP, Truog RD. History of Medicine: The DNR Order after 40 Years. N Engl J Med 2016;375:504-506.

by Carl F. Frost, Ph.D., a psychologist who, after service in the U.S. Navy in WWII, joined Douglas McGregor and the Department of Industrial Relations at the Massachusetts Institute of Technology, where he met Joseph N. Scanlon. In the 1930's, Scanlon had been a union leader at a Pittsburgh steel mill battered by the Depression and heading to go out of business. Scanlon convinced top management, workers, and his union to approach the challenge by focusing on mutual cooperation. The workers' knowledge and participation proved critical for increasing productivity, reducing waste, and improving quality of items produced, advantages that saved the mill and led to gains in profit, wages, and working conditions. With that success, Scanlon moved up in the United Steelworkers union, working to spread more widely the approach he had initiated at the mill. He emphasized cooperation between labor and management, the importance of each worker having a voice in how he or she did his or her job, and broad representation of workers at meetings with top management.

Several Midwest factories adopted what became known as The Scanlon Plan. Learning of this brought us to Dr. Frost. Even after a couple of his visits with us at BI, the clarity conveyed by Dr. Frost seemed to match neither his enthusiasm nor our capacity to grasp clearly what the Plan actually entailed. He convinced us to see for ourselves by traveling to Zeeland, Michigan and its Herman Miller furniture factory. Warmly welcomed by Max DePree, then CEO and later board chair, and Richard Ruch, CFO and later CEO, several BI vice presidents and I spent a few revealing days of observation and discussion with them and others. Among the positive impressions were the mutual familiarity and easy interaction the company executives had with a wide spectrum of employees as we walked through the various work areas. Even more so was their comment, backed by the workers, that no product had ever left the Herman Miller plant that had not been improved either in design or production efficiency by workers on the factory floor.

A revealing incident surfaced when we walked into the shipping area and asked a worker what was important about his job. A tough-looking, extravagantly tattooed dude, he wasted no time in response.

"What's important about my job? Don't you understand? See that desk over there? It's cherry wood. It has right hand drawers. Suppose I sent it out maple with left hand drawers? The customer gets mad sends it back. We pay the freight and he tells friends how sloppy Herman Miller is. It eats into our profit. Do you think that guy is going to buy again from Herman Miller? No, he'll go to Steelcase across town or maybe even from Korea where they make something no way as good as ours, ship it from there, and still charge twenty to thirty percent below our fair price. So the question is, do we want to be a company makes great furniture and employs several hundred folks, or become an importer of not-so-great furniture and employs only twenty? Because of my mistake? That's what's important about my job!"

It hit me, "This guy owns the company!" We began to understand what Dr. Frost meant about employees "… owning the problem…" and asked him to work with us on a plan for Beth Israel Hospital, a challenge unique because we then had over 2,800 employees while the Midwest factories incorporating the Scanlon Plan generally employed only 200 or so workers at any one site.

How to begin? First we had to educate ourselves and then employees and staff at all levels exactly what is The Scanlon Plan. As described in *The Scanlon Plan for Organization Development, Identity, Participation and Equity,*[27] it is based on three conditions essential for the well-functioning organization:

- Identification with the company by all employees, and an understanding of how one's job and department relate to the mission of the company.

---

[27] Frost CF, Wakely JH, Ruh RA. The Scanlon Plan for Organization Development, Identification, Participation, and Equity. 1974, East Lansing, MI., Michigan State University Press.

- The opportunity for all employees to assume responsibility for improving the workplace and its output. Change is treated as inevitable. Wide participation in planning for and creating change is fostered through an open suggestion system, a committee structure for encouraging and evaluating suggestions for change, systems for acting on those suggestions, and communicating on actions taken and their results.
- The economic and psychological equity of all employees. They should be kept aware of how the company is doing overall and when quality or productivity improve. Rewards should be determined fairly and distributed equitably through sharing any resulting gains.

We began with education; this was not a program simply to be mandated. We oriented middle managers, then gathered groups of employees, no more than eight or ten at a time, beginning each session underscoring the need for positive change as we faced the challenges ahead. We described the principles of The Scanlon Plan and then, after questions at each session, asked attendees to vote, responding to two questions: (1) Do you think we should explore further the possible opportunity offered by The Scanlon Plan? (2) If so, would you be willing to elect a group of your peers among you to develop specifics of a plan we could then consider up or down for us at the BI? We used written ballots so that no individual's vote would be influenced by another. We titled the program, "P R E P A R E / 2 1" to reflect our heading into the 21st century.

The overwhelmingly positive response led to the next step, employees nominating seventy-five individuals from all segments of the hospital to form three groups of twenty-five, each tasked to develop a document explaining one of the three major components of The Scanlon Plan:

- Identity: Who we are at Boston's Beth Israel Hospital and where we are heading.

- Participation: How employees' suggestions will be evaluated and how information about suggestions offered and resulting actions will be made known throughout the organization.
- Equity: How any monetary gains resulting from suggestions implemented will be shared among employees and the hospital.

These groups put together a document in English, Spanish, and Haitian Creole, presenting the plan as they envisioned it for our hospital. Each page carried a column displaying a corresponding matching executive summary to help foster broad understanding.

Our hospital board had been alerted early to this effort and its rationale. With the P/21 Plan details finished, we sought their final approval. Some board members were hesitant, concerned about our non-profit organization sharing any improved operating bottom line with employees. We assured them we would not play games with the hospital's budget, arguing that what P/21 could produce would be "found money," typically from new direct cost-savings on an already tight existing budget, new-found money-saving ideas through the P/21 participation process, or admissions over a realistic but already stretched budget. Any monetary gains directly related to P/21 improvements made would be shared fifty-fifty, half for the hospital, half for the employees but also with a hold-back of some portion so that the process is temperate. The board gave us its vote of confidence.

With the Plan underway, a timely series of publications kept employees aware of suggestions offered, those implemented and any resulting gains in dollars or other measures of improvement such as time saved, efficiency of care processes, simplification of material and administrative processes, etc. The calculation of cash rewards was detailed regularly, making it understandable when there were rewards and when not. The dollars gained were modest, distributed to all employees, and issued through checks differing in color from our standard pay check, to emphasize the importance of employees' personal contribution to the hospital's mission.

Annually we benefited from an on-site review by an impressive task force asked to evaluate P/21 and offer their recommendations for improvement. The visitors included Warren Bennis, Distinguished Professor, University of Southern California; Max DePree, CEO, Herman Miller; Robert McKersie, Professor of Industrial Relations, Sloan School, Massachusetts Institute of Technology; Seymour Sarason, Emeritus Professor of Psychology, Yale University; John Chilingerian, Professor of Management, Brandeis University; and management consultant Eileen Shapiro, Hillcrest Group, Cambridge, Massachusetts.

The results of our effort were impressive. The spirit of inquiry and participation for the sake of improvement were heightened, as was cooperation among diverse groups and departments. Employees and medical staff took seriously the phrase offered by Dr. Frost, "The opportunity and responsibility to influence, to the extent of one's capability." Success in gaining efficiency, cutting costs, improving quality, and fostering cooperation among diverse departments heightened job satisfaction, pride in achievement, and personal commitment to the hospital's mission. An example of the coalescence of several groups involved in a patient care system examining an issue of inefficiency and then working together to deal with it successfully was presented in 2002 in a workshop at the Massachusetts Institute of Technology.[28]

We began our exploration of The Scanlon Plan in 1986. For top management to fathom it, determine to give it a solid try, educate staff and employees, develop the details, secure support from the hospital board, and implement the plan, the process took several years. Going live in October 1989, PREPARE/21 continued evolving positively. Upon our 1996 merger with New England Deaconess Hospital, as with our program in Primary Nursing, we understood that P/21 could not simply be extended as such by decree to the new employees under our merged roof. But with BI employees long involved in the plan now scat-

[28] Rabkin MT, Avakian L. Enhancing Patient Care Through Enhancing Employee Voice. Reflections on the Scanlon Plan at Boston's Beth Israel Medical Center. Ed: Cass SC. Working Paper #WPD0002. Spring 2002 Seminar Series. MIT Workplace Center, Cambridge, MA.

tered across both campuses, much of its principles and practices do remain, particularly:

- Persons doing the job are among the most effective in understanding how their work can be made more efficient.
- It is important employees and medical staff feel free to contribute to improvement and that their suggestions call for serious consideration and feedback.
- Management gains substantially when employees and staff at all levels identify with our mission, feel a meaningful part of our organization, and are comfortable with the opportunity and responsibility to contribute to its betterment.

COMPETITIVE ADVANTAGE
BIFF, THE "BETH ISRAEL FAMILY AND FRIENDS" LIST

For many people, the hospital can offer an experience less than comfortable, despite good intentions of its staff. Neither bed nor pillow offer the familiarity of home, and one must wait, not necessarily that long but seeming so, for a glass of water or help to the bedpan or bathroom. The food may seem bland, cold, unfamiliar. One is asked frequently to give name, date of birth, etc., something important to avoid misidentification, but its repetition can seem pointless to the patient. A physician making rounds may pull back the sheet to listen to your chest or feel your abdomen, then leave without replacing the covers. Another may stand tall while addressing you in bed rather than sitting to converse at a coequal level. Strange new things tend to happen at the seeming convenience of one's caregivers, dietary staff, room cleaners, and the like. In short one is no longer master of his or her own life.

To help counteract issues that make for loss of one's sense of identity, independence, even adulthood, we generated a "BIFF" list (Beth Israel Family and Friends) of inpatients, intended to help convey the hospital's warmth and strengthen a sense of personalization for the patient. Our list daily identified a broad category of inpatients, anyone with some connection, close or distant to the hospital. Including all present and past trustees, medical staff, employees, volunteers, and their family members, it added other contacts of employees and staff of whom we became aware, along with government officials, notable persons, and of course, donors. BIFF patients might be visited by me or other administrators and/or staff from Public Affairs or Development. Care was taken not to impose on those whose illness warranted leaving them alone or were too early in their hospitalization to visit.

An employee, physician, nurse, trustee, or former patient might have alerted us about a relative, friend, perhaps their child's school teacher, or their plumber about to be admitted, and that person would be included and visited. It was meaningful when one of us dropped by, opening with, "I learned from ____ that you are their gardener. They mentioned you were coming to BI. I happen to be the chief (or whatever) and wanted to say hello. How are things going?" A brief chat would follow. Most patients were pleased, gaining a sense of identity and connection otherwise unexpected. There was never solicitation, only casual conversation letting patients know they were recognized as someone with a connection, close or remote. The hospital visitor might leave a business card with name and phone number, a token that could reassure the patient of a new and unexpected avenue to which they had access should they feel the need.

Early on, a few nurses voiced concern that patients might be singled out for implied special treatment but soon became reassured that was not so. The BIFF list was simply one more effort to take down a notch or two the depersonalization inherent in so many hospitalizations. Other actions offering "anchoring" and comfort also began early at BI, such as switching the corkboard, designed to hold the grandchildren's get-well sketches, from behind the head of the bed where the patient couldn't see it to the wall near the foot of the bed where, along with specific room number and phone number, calendar, clock, and name of the patient's lead doctor and nurse on each shift, all could be seen and appreciated by the patient. Now such information is commonly displayed with thoughtful visibility at hospitals elsewhere. Menu choices and serving times have become more responsive to patient's appetites.

I've received comments from patients, even years after hospitalization, on how meaningful such efforts were. Now with HIPAA (Health Insurance Portability and Accountability Act of 1996), unsolicited visits from administrators and others not involved in direct service to the patient are deemed intrusions on their privacy. Fortunately, our intent to strengthen personalization remains shared by the medical and nursing staff but also by staff in housekeeping, nutrition, transport, and others both with and without direct patient contact. That may relate to the fact that staff at all levels are kept aware not only of the hospital's mission but also of what is going on daily to fulfill it. (See the section on Newsletters.) Because the demographic distribution of our patients is fairly comparable to that of our hospital personnel overall, some patients may be more comfortable interacting with hospital staff with whom they feel more in common than with their doctor or nurse. Thus, the BIFF effort continues, modified but remaining as one more of meaningful ways to help distinguish our care.

COMPETITIVE ADVANTAGE
THE CENTER FOR EDUCATION

Early in 1996, Harvard Medical School Dean Dr. Daniel C. Tosteson and I huddled over shared concerns, particularly:

- Escalating growth in knowledge of medicine and basic science and its increasing complexity. Neither student nor teacher can now encompass it all.
- Burgeoning growth in complexity of the technology and equipment applied to diagnosis and treatment.

- Increasing time physicians must spend on administrative detail, complicated further by use of computers distancing them from face-to-face contact with patients, detracting from effective doctor-patient interaction at least in some instances.

What to do? Together we focused on how best the physician, expert or novice, will contend with these pressures, particularly the enlarging content and complexity of knowledge. Harvard Medical School's response focused on curricular reform, with Dr. Tosteson initiating (and later deans adding) impressive series of improvements in content, format, and delivery.

We recognized that at neither our hospitals nor most medical schools were there meaningful efforts in teaching theory or practice of adult education. Yet the academic demands on hospital faculty, from intern to full professor, argue for sophisticated understanding of what and how we teach, its methods, goals, and effectiveness. A trenchant scenario offered by Dr. Richard M. Schwartzstein opens our hospital's annual welcoming session to newly-arrived first-year residents. He asked how many had children, and a few hands were raised.

"Now," he went on, "let's assume it's first day of kindergarten. You're chatting with the very pleasant teacher and ask, 'What qualifies you to teach my child?' Her answer, 'Well, when I was in kindergarten, I got an A.' How reassuring would that be?"

Dr. Schwartzstein added, "Yet that is what we levy on you. Yesterday you were a fourth-year student but today, an intern and faculty member of Harvard Medical School, responsible for helping educate its fourth-year students on their hospital rotations. You got an A in Medicine. But what do you know about teaching? About adult education? From here on, you will not only practice medicine, you'll be teaching! That's why we include adult learning and teaching along with everything else on your plate."

In mid-1996, Harvard Medical School and Beth Israel established a joint program, the Institute for Teaching and Research, shortly to become the Carl J. Shapiro Institute for Teaching and Research, thanks to a generous gift of support. Located at Beth Israel, its "teaching and research" would focus on medical education. First headed by Dr. Michael Rosenblatt, then Dr. Steven Weinberger, the Institute grew slowly, in part because of time taken to clarify to individual clinical department leadership that the Institute would not usurp their teaching responsibilities. The Institute was there to help strengthen, enrich understanding, and support fulfilment of their efforts. With range and depth of its activities developing under current leadership by Dr. Schwartzstein, its Executive Director and the Ellen and Melvin Gordon Professor of Medicine and Medical Education at HMS, the Institute has blossomed to become the BIDMC Center for Education.

Today the Center for Education is a hospital leader in medical education and scholarship at HMS and its hospitals, and both nationally and beyond. Facing the rapid accumulation of overwhelming amounts of medical information, today's medical student and physician cannot know it all. They must access and then evaluate well beyond their own store of immediately retrievable knowledge or facility at clinical pattern recognition. Focusing on critical thinking in medical and nursing care, the Center defines critical thinking as "... the ability to apply higher-order cognitive skills (conceptualization, analysis, evaluation) and the disposition to be deliberate about thinking (being open-minded and intellectually honest) that lead to action... logical and appropriate."[29] A recent detailed review from the Center for Education discusses the challenges in teaching clinical reasoning, its underlying cognitive principles, strategies in teaching clinical thinking, and incorporating its use in clinical practice.[30]

Other Center for Education activities include extending its mutually developed strategic plan for education throughout all medical

---

[29] Papp KK, Huang GC, Lauzon Clabo LM, Delva D, Fischer M, Konopasek L, Schwartzstein RM, Gusie M. Milestones of Critical Thinking: A Developmental Model for Medicine and Nursing. Acad Med. 2014;89:715-720.

[30] Richards JB, Hayes MM, Schwartzstein RM. Teaching Clinical Reasoning and Critical Thinking: From Cognitive Theory to Practical Application. Chest. 2020;158(4):1617-1628. doi: 10.1016/j.chest.2020.05.525. Epub 2020 May 22. Accessed 31 December 2020.

departments, a simulation center teaching and enhancing hands-on skills, dealing with unexpected emergencies in patient care whether medical, environmental, or personal, interactive case-based conferences for medical students designed to integrate clinical and pre-clinical learning, promote inductive reasoning and enhance students' capacity as peer teachers and in their personal interactions with patients and families. The Center offers courses in medical education for local, national, and international audiences and periodic competitively admitted multi-institutional retreats on specific topics in medical education with follow-up implementations by attendee schools. It has developed an annual fellowship on teaching for young faculty from all HMS-affiliated hospitals, provides counseling on academic career development with special attention to minority and LGBT students and faculty. Its faculty has a strong presence teaching both basic science and clinical medicine at the medical school and at the hospital, carries out research studies on educational methods and content. Enriching the hospital's support for both teaching and clinical practice, the Center for Education has become an effective resource for young faculty seeking both excellence and scholarship as teachers.

COMPETITIVE ADVANTAGE
THE NEWSLETTERS

News, conjectures, and rumors abound in any institution. Topics vary — decisions made or anticipated, actions and praise for individuals from top management to entry level, any extant content on hospital and related issues from fact to speculation to fantasy, along with editorial comment. I wanted to be as open as possible about what I knew was taking place at the hospital or about to, and our relationships with Harvard Medical School, nearby institutions, and the community we serve. It was important that staff and employees share in news from my office and timely so. Because patients come from the spread of social and economic levels similar to that of our employees and staff, some will feel more comfortable with hospital staff other than their doctor or nurse and converse with them more readily even about their own health and perhaps other hospital matters. Should employees feel uninformed about our mission, achievements, challenges, current and planned activities, or unable to answer or know how to direct elsewhere inquiries from a patient, it is likely they will feel distant from the hospital family. Because staff are critical to our mission, all employees and affiliated physicians should be kept informed.

One example to help strengthen the inclusion of entry-level employees, Vice President for Nursing Joyce Clifford changed deployment of housekeeping, transportation and dietary workers. Instead of tasks daily scattered randomly throughout the hospital, those employees were assigned specific nursing units. Our nurses often took lunch breaks in a retreat room on their unit floor. They welcomed the now-stationed dietary, housekeeping, and transportation workers to do the same and many did, strengthening their identification with the nursing staff, their awareness of ongoing hospital activities, and the meaningfulness of their roles. The consistent placement fostered identification with patients on "their" floor, illustrated by the comment of a transporter, "No one is going to let my patient wait in a cold area without a blanket."

A more general effort began some years earlier. From arrival I wrote two newsletters, an "Employee Newsletter" and the "Dear Doctor." Each edition was on one sheet of paper published weekly. The "Employee Newsletter" offered detail on patient service and running the hospital. It included relevant information on clinical care and scholarship intrinsic to our role as a research-intensive major teaching hospital affiliated with Harvard Medical School. This newsletter was published in three languages, English, Spanish, and Haitian Creole, thanks to diligence and alacrity from a pair of devoted translators. Content of the "Dear Doctor" emphasized patient service and clinical care, offered more on research, teaching, and related academic issues but did not ignore hospital administrative and human stories issues.

Distributed throughout the hospital and in bulk to managers who shared the newsletters with supervisors and thence employees during staff meetings, they led to discussions to encourage clarification. "Dear Doctor" went throughout the hospital, too, and by mail to outside offices. These newsletters were ways to emphasize repeatedly the hospital's mission, philosophy, and activities, keeping employees and staff alert to major plans and actions along with the daily life of the institution. At times we complimented individuals for exemplary actions. There were occasional cautionary notes, without specific naming and infrequently, a bit of humor.

A few samples are offered:

- The beginning of a new academic year is always a stimulating time. We harken to the oncoming crispness of air of a late autumn evening, anticipate new challenges, prepare for the arrival of students, and hope for at least a modest measure of success. My former Professor of Medicine, the late Dr. Walter Bauer, commented that there were only two questions we need ask, if they be answered with candor:
  1. How can I best help this patient?
  2. In doing so, what can I learn?

  Implicit in this credo is the understanding that we also learn by teaching, and we teach in part by example. I believe that the coming years will be exciting ones at Beth Israel Hospital, that we will grow in academic excellence, and that such excellence will be the fundamental basis for better care of more patients.

Dear Doctor, September 7th, 1966

- This week's issue submits two drawings for your comment. From our architects, the first sketch proposes single and double room designs in the new patient building. Note that the bathroom is "outboard" to save nursing steps from corridor to patient, that there is also a sink within the room as one exits (as well as one in the bathroom of course); that the chase between bathrooms will allow new services to be brought up; that the column arrangement allows maximum flexibility. The larger plan overleaf is a proposed design for a typical inpatient floor.

These studies represent a good start, I believe. What we need now are your comments, not only from physicians and nurses but from all personnel whose work takes them onto the inpatient units and also from anyone else who, by virtue of enthusiasm, interest, insight, knowledge, experience as a patient, or desire to participate, has something to add.

Don't delay. Make your comments right on this sheet and send them to my office. Please sign it unless you would prefer not to. This is your opportunity to influence what may well become our most important building.

Employee Newsletter, August 19th, 1969

- Recently one of our patients happened to be the father-in-law of a physician who had been an intern and then assistant resident at Beth Israel Hospital nearly two decades ago. This physician is now prominent at a major university hospital in the West. He wrote to the two BI physicians who cared for his father-in-law. I want to share with you part of those letters.

"The attitudes manifested by *all* of the personnel at the Beth Israel Hospital were amazing to observe in a major teaching institution. I have never seen that kind of care in any other teaching hospital in this country.... Your decision to hospitalize him at BI proved to be an incredibly wise decision for him and the family. None of us has ever experienced a hospital in which so much caring was demonstrated by *all* of the personnel. Thank you again for all of your efforts for all of us."

Dear Doctor, July 27th, 1978

- The fresh format of this letterhead presents the new logo for Beth Israel Hospital and introduces one of the standard formats for hospital stationery now being adopted to provide consistency and clarity in our appearance on the written page. This was developed under Mr. J. Antony Swartz-Lloyd, director of public affairs, who describes the change as follows:

"The new Beth Israel Hospital symbol derives from three familiar sources: the caduceus or snake-entwined staff, a symbol of medicine from classical mythology; the double helix, a representation of the building block basic to life: and the B and I of Beth Israel. Together these images represent our hospital and its dual role fostering the art of healing and furthering scholarship in biomedical science through teaching and research."

Dear Doctor, April 24th, 1980

- This week's trial of the men accused of the murder of Beth Israel nurse ___ brings up a host of intense feelings from that tragedy of last March. The passage of time has not helped us to make any peace with that sad event. I find, in myself, that the sorrow and the fury have not at all diminished, and I suspect we shall never come to rest with those feelings, for something in us all was murdered in that horror. No statement, no sorrow, no punishment can restore the profound loss. Only the memory of a brave young woman who lost everything can hint at some small measure of, perhaps, hope as we try to fulfill the ideals of goodness, compassion and beauty which were hers.

Employee Newsletter, October 22nd, 1981

- A warm salute goes to members of our laundry staff, long known for their high productivity, outstanding quality of work, general helpfulness, and friendly spirit. Last week they demonstrated remarkable ability to respond to a crisis. Several days ago, as a result of construction activities, the inevitable lint on top of a duct caught fire and the danger of a major conflagration flared in seconds. Led by Mr. Louis Parial, Manager of the Laundry, and with the help of Mr. Ricardo Fernandez of Transportation, who happened to be there at that moment, the staff put out the fire, removed themselves from danger, and began evacuating the smoke even before the very timely arrival of the Boston Fire Department. And the day's production figures were not affected! Hats off to the laundry for cool heads, quick hands, and a classy performance in the face of an emergency that could have spelled bad trouble.

Employee Newsletter, September 26th, 1984

- Interesting comment from a patient I recently visited, "Why is it that nurses always introduce themselves, but when a group of physicians and medical students troop in to stand around the bedside, they seem to feel that their names don't count?" Previously I have railed against addressing patients by their first names, arguing that one should use the first name only in situations in which you wish to be addressed in the same familiar manner. I'd argue that by giving the patient your name, you imply your words and actions directed to the patient will be of sufficient virtue that you are pleased to have your name associated with the effort. It is only common courtesy to do so and particularly for the team leader to introduce all the others.

Dear Doctor, December 17th, 1985

- A health care consultant's newsletter, "Health Care Strategist," cites Peter Drucker, a well-known business consultant. Mr. Drucker's comments on getting best performance from everyone in the organization seemed to me to parallel the philosophy in our program, PREPARE 21. Would you agree?

"It's not enough to hire good people." In <u>The Practice of Management</u>, Peter Drucker continues, "Even the best people work up to capacity only if they feel part of a worthwhile enterprise, with their contributions both recognized and valued. There are ways to create such a feeling. First. demand high performance — not minimum acceptable, not average, high. Nothing gives people more pride of workmanship and accomplishment. Second, pile on information. He (or she) should know how he (or she) is doing without being told. Finally, encourage the development of a managerial vision. The worker will assume responsibility for peak performance only if he (or she) sees the enterprise as if he (or she) were a manager responsible, through performance, for its success and survival. Employees should be expected to act like owners, working as if the company depended on their efforts, doing whatever needs to be done."

The "...as if..." surprises me. Here at BI, the Hospital surely does depend on your efforts, and not only for our primary mission of patient care. Many of us are "customers" of other departments within the hospital; we depend upon each other to create the overall high quality of performance at Boston's Beth Israel.

Employee Newsletter, August 18th, 1988

- Here's a bit from a patient's letter worth mulling over — kudos for the nursing staff, all of whom took pains not to wake the patient in the next bed, but none for the physician who did not: "This short stay showed me enough to estimate the worth of your nurses. They are wonderful and thoughtful. Example: I had been awakened in the early A.M. when a doctor who wanted to examine my roommate in the further bed snapped on the room's overhead lights unnecessarily, then went into her area and put her lights on. I asked him to shut off mine. Unfortunately, I was then awake for the day. In about an hour, I heard little quiet steps and saw a nurse who needed to check a chart. She carried a little flashlight, disturbing no one. Do you see the difference? And every single nurse during my stay showed the same thoughtfulness. I hope you appreciate your nursing staff, they are jewels."

Dear Doctor, May 9th, 1989

- Here's an important excerpt in a letter from a health care professional. While speaking of nursing, the writer makes a point relevant to any of us — in any role — who come in contact with patients. She writes, "...there is one aspect of nursing care I want to tell you about. When I was in the holding area being readied for surgery, the last thing I remember was a woman bending over me saying, 'My name is Paula Steele. I will be your nurse while you are having your surgery, and I will take care of you.' This was truly heartwarming. It brings to mind that we seldom see the people behind the masks in the OR, nor do we probably give appropriate recognition for what they do for us.... I will never forget that..."

How reassuring to the patient to hear that phrase, "I will be (or am) your ___, and I will take care of you."

Employee Newsletter. February 1st, 1996

- Perhaps the item most commented on (to me) surfaced annually shortly before Thanksgiving: Two widespread misconceptions about physicians held by the laity seem to be (a) that all are skilled at surgery, particularly on Thanksgiving, and (b) therefore physicians carve the bird better than others at the annual repast. This can be problematic for newly minted physicians. First-year residents especially bask in a glow of traditional admiration during pre-dinner cocktails, unaware that eyes will be on them as the (not uncommonly dull) carving knife and fork are thrust into their hands at the encouragement of a ravenous crowd. It may be especially daunting for our new residents from abroad, where the closest thing to whole roast turkey they may have encountered was Chicken McNuggets. And when the result is more like hash than elegant and even slices, the warm glow of pre-dinner sherry chills far too soon. That is no way for our young physicians to suffer Thanksgiving!

So, to avoid such discomfiture (and to sustain the reputation of BI, of course), here is a set of simple instructions cadged from a Time-Life volume, shrunk in size to be placed inconspicuously on the table (or fit the inside lining of one's jacket), yet sufficient in clarity to enable you to carve with *eclat*. Good luck, and please pass the gravy! (A set of line drawings and related instructions followed.)

Dear Doctor, November 14th, 1989

Early on I wondered were these missives appreciated, particularly within a few hours of distribution when I would spot a few, always on colored paper, visible in wastebaskets. Over time I received requests from trustees, directors of distant hospitals, and others for copies, but what ultimately convinced me were comments, made by someone long departed from the hospital, on how much they valued those weekly bulletins.

Today with computers throughout the hospital, information sharing is largely digital and through posters in well-traveled areas. While efficient as methods of dissemination, computers may have limited reach to employees at entry level. And in the press of other priorities, the challenge and cost become prohibitive for translation into the growing number of first languages among our increasingly multicultural employees and staff. The computer could assist with translation, but the plethora of technical terms might be problematic. Newsletters are only one component of management's transparency toward medical, nursing, and other staff; other efforts are required. The keys to communication are visibility, candor, relevance, frequency, and recency. As stated by Max DePree, then CEO of Herman Miller, Inc., "The first responsibility of a leader is to define reality."[31]

COMPETITIVE ADVANTAGE
THE SEARCH FOR ACADEMIC DEPARTMENT CHAIRS

When a department chair or other tenured professor retires or leaves, the Harvard Medical School dean appoints a search committee. Usually led by a tenured faculty member from the institution where the successful candidate will work, a BI committee would include several of our tenured faculty, one or two from other HMS-affiliated teaching hospitals, and one or two from the basic science or other departments of the medical school or university. Their charge, to find the best person possible, begins with various sources contributing to forge a description of the department, review its strengths and weaknesses, and its role within the hospital and Harvard Medical School. With department members and others, I would then develop a detailed job description for the committee's use. Identifying related experts worldwide, the committee would seek their views on future directions for the discipline and for our department, and suggestions of possible candidates. Some might be contacted later for opinion on potential finalists. At an early committee meeting, the departing professor is asked for his or her views of the department's strengths and weaknesses, and the future directions it should take. This may prove more or less useful but is, at minimum, a courtesy not to shun. As potential candidates are vetted, some are in-

---

[31] DePree M, Leadership Is An Art. 1987, East Lansing, MI. Michigan State University Press.

vited to visit the hospital, gain directly a sense of the department, the opportunity envisioned, and meet various other department chairs, administrators, and colleagues with whom he or she will work. A final few spend time with the medical school dean. Ultimately the search committee makes its recommendation to the dean who moves it through the university hierarchy where the appointment, now presumably well-vetted, almost always is confirmed.

An ongoing search can be an anxious time within the department. Who will be the new chair? What's life to be like under the new leader? Would the character of the department and the roles of those remaining be as favorable as each might hope? Rumors easily surface, some generating concern among those rightly or not feeling vulnerable.

This became apparent when a department member, visibly distressed, appeared in my office to proclaim that the "new choice" meant the end of quality in his department. Yet at that moment, the committee had not even assembled its list of possible candidates! To lessen anxiety I asked the faculty of that department other than its chair to select among them two or three members to form a temporary task force free to contact me as the search progressed. As an *ex officio* member of the search committee, I could respond to rumors, and within limits, keep department members up-to-date on the state of the search.

That departmental task force offered a second benefit. Invited to visit the hospital, candidates would meet with department members and others, present some of their own work, and offer views of the discipline's future and the directions we might consider taking. Because a department member, regardless of promised anonymity, might hesitate voicing negative judgment on a candidate who might shortly become his or her chief, it seemed better for the task force members to convey to me and thus the search committee the variety of department members' responses without identifying any individual. A dominant sentiment usually developed on each candidate but dissident views also registered. Keeping department members in the information loop and giving each the option of an unconstrained voice helped ease the inevitable tension of a search.

Professional search firms are engaged occasionally in academic searches. They can approach an individual they or the committee members have identified who may not have been thinking about a move, even probe potential interest or current restiveness before revealing identity of the institution seeking the chair. Another advantage is ability of the search consultant seeing possible candidates in their home environment where both direct observation and less obvious casual inquiry can offer insight. (I have visited hospitals where, while walking the corridors with its CEO there was barely recognition of the CEO by employees we passed, while at others warm two-way conversations were initiated by the employees.) But because cost-effectiveness from the search consultant's viewpoint lies in getting a candidate selected and placed as timely as possible, one must respond carefully to their enthusiasm. There are other cautions. Some academicians elsewhere may hesitate to comment on a candidate with anything less than enthusiasm. On occasion referral sources may be supportive through interest in seeing the candidate depart from their own institution. In one search, we had high marks in a reference letter about a candidate. A decade later, our chair of that search committee, in casual conversation with that letter's author, mentioned that the individual did not perform as had been expected from references.

The writer commented, "You should have contacted me. I would have told you about that person."

Once it appears selection and acceptance are in the offing, my role as hospital CEO would intensify. Commitments are to be made, some by the Medical School dean but most by our hospital (Harvard Medical School affiliated hospitals are largely financially independent of the school.) From time spent with the final candidate, I would draft a letter describing accountabilities of the role, the commitments I felt we had discussed, both by me representing the hospital and those vouchsafed by the candidate. This went to twenty or more double-spaced pages. It would include dollar support and its timing, typically over a three-year annual projection to accompany plans for new faculty and other positions, programs, space, and equipment. Received by the candidate, it was to be reworked to his or her satisfaction. Together we would go over the edited draft working on points unclear or divergent, and negotiate those not yet reaching agreement. This back-and-forth process of editing, discussing, and further editing repeated until we reached consensus with formal agreement confirmed in a document we both signed. Out of this process were virtually no instances where the candidate, now incumbent, or I charged the other with not adhering to our consensual commitments. Working together we forged a common understanding of the roles, actions, and relationships of both candidate and management, commitment to the hospital's mission, the new chair's plans for the department, when and how they would be implemented. Almost always our department chairs have been outstanding.

The division of financial support mentioned above — the bulk coming from the hospital rather than the medical school — is not unique, but it is unusual. One of its consequences is that a hospital can feel more able to act independently than if governed by the dean. Years ago at one of the HMS-affiliated hospitals, its CEO voiced the intention to move its affiliation from Harvard to MIT, perhaps more a declaration of bravado than one of independence. At BI we worked hand-in-hand with the medical school dean, and while quibbling at times over details of medical school dollar support, differences of viewpoint never soured the beneficial bilateral relationship.

Most of our medical school deans have commented on the fiscal independence enjoyed by its affiliated hospitals, at times leading to behaviors contrary to their wishes or their views of the best interests of the school and hospitals collectively. And there have been occasional moves by one or two hospitals acting in their own narrow interest to disadvantage other affiliated hospitals or the medical school. At times remedies have been found by the hospitals or the dean. For example, when the designation of trauma units was underway, and only one was declared to be allocated to the Longwood area which includes Beth Israel, Brigham and Women's, and Children's hospitals, the announcement by one that it would apply alone was followed by the voiced intention of the other two to do the same, noting that the outcome would likely result in no designation at all. That led to the two adult hospitals agreeing to share the designation (for example receiving trauma and other patients arriving by helicopter on alternate weeks), which was appropriate because each provided the requisite quality of service, had comparable clinical faculty, teaching and training responsibilities. Both adult hospitals then insisted, since neither serves infants and children save neonates, that sending desperately ill children from their ERs to adjacent Children's Hospital while medically necessary was unwise clinically and therefore Children's Hospital must be included as well. The designation then went to all three institutions. Another example — when one institution decided to apply for a major NIH grant but could do so only through the medical school, the dean refused to approve it until all the other research-intensive affiliated institutions were included. This not only strengthened the application but advanced its likelihood of competitive success. Both opportunities clearly had a *quid pro quo* for their achievement. It is notable that most such instances seem to emerge out of administrative actions although physicians may have been the trigger; inter-institutional cooperation among individual scientists and clinicians in general tends not to reek of similar selfishness. (At one point, somewhat disheartened by such internecine folly, when I was asked about the state of cooperation among the affiliated hospitals, I replied, "In the old days, it was dog-eat-dog; now just the reverse is true.")

Thinking about the dean's dilemma of encouraging cooperation, I recall a meeting of the Council of Teaching Hospitals of the Association of American Medical Colleges. A group of hospital CEOs was addressed by Norman R. Augustine, then Chairman and CEO of Lockheed Martin. Talking about the importance of hearing the diversity of thinking and views from his subordinates and other relevant experts before coming to a decision, he offered, "I put all that together, reach a conclusion, then share my decision and they carry it out."

One hospital CEO raised his hand, "I do the same — get my chiefs of service together, ask them. 'What do you think, etc. I listen, then I say, okay, here's what we'll do.' What follows is they stand up and, walking out, ask each other, 'Now do we work for him or does he work for us?' Could that happen at Lockheed Martin?"

Mr. Augustine's response, "Only once."

Obviously the relationship between the HMS dean and the CEOs of its affiliated hospitals doesn't parallel the command of the CEO with his/her immediate subordinates in organizations such as Lockheed Martin. Yet in my opinion, the dean does hold a compelling option. Let's go back to the appointment of a tenured hospital-based faculty member. It is in the hands of the hospital-based search committee and that of the hospital, but only until the choice is sent to the medical school dean for review and forwarding to higher echelons of the university. At that point, the dean has control.

Taking a leaf from former President Lyndon B. Johnson, suppose the dean takes this friendly stand, "That's a great appointment you're proposing, and I stand behind the quality of your selection. But I do have one concern. From my reading of the powers above me, they don't seem to be happy with (what you have done or refused to do.) That particular action of yours they seem to feel may not be in the best interests of the medical school and our hospitals overall. There seems to be enough feeling they may want to hold off approval of this appointment, as great as it actually is, until that other issue is straightened out."

I go back to the question as put to Mr. Augustine, "Could this happen at HMS?" And the answer is, I suggest, "Only once."

COMPETITIVE ADVANTAGE
A WHIZ-BANG SABBATICAL PROGRAM

Here's a proposal I tried to hatch, without success but still keep hoping... These are tough times for academic health centers (medical schools and their affiliated major research-intensive teaching hospitals). No greater challenge faces the department chair where top performance is critical for patient care, teaching, and research scholarship. Other institutional responsibilities demand attention, particularly planning for the future and finding ways and means to carry it out. He or she must provide the vision and substance requisite for department leadership, counsel and support career growth of department members and serve as role model, especially for younger department members. And while not necessarily expert in every aspect of clinical practice and teaching and research, the department chair must approach the ideal in at least one and have the awareness and refined taste to identify, recruit, support, and manage high quality throughout his/her department.

Because department chairs exist on never-ending clinical, scientific, and administrative treadmills, opportunity can be limited for reflection on the evolving currents of change they confront. This can lead to untimely departure, with resulting turnover expensive to the academic health center and at times inimical to positive change. As with any organization, new blood is not necessarily better, particularly when the current occupant offers superior intellect, sensitivity, imagination, and ability as leader and manager. How best can we foster continuing exercise of the superior qualities and positive impact of such individuals? How can the academic health center avoid loss of a chairperson of surpassing excellence? How best can his/her creativity and capability be sustained?

Time for thoughtful reflection is needed to position one's department for its future, but once realistic and positive changes are conceptualized, they are neither easy to fund nor simple to achieve. The academic chair needs time to step back, project, and visualize the department's future in light of ongoing and anticipated developments in clinical practice, teaching, research, funding, etc., envision what must be done to strengthen excellence in care, scholarship, resilience, creativity, efficiency, and morale and then find ways and means to implement the progress envisioned. It is no small task!

Sabbatical leave offers an opportunity to re-charge one's intellectual batteries. While traditionally the period away is to focus on personal scholarship, a more encompassing effort is needed now for leadership of a major academic medical department; today's rapidly evolving world of medical practice, teaching and research demands refreshing the department's vision and capability every few years.

After leaving my CEO role, I worked in our Institute for Education and Research described earlier. Its focus is on the study and improvement of teaching and learning in medicine. In its stimulating environment, I thought about how to extend opportunities of the conventional academic sabbatical program to meet more effectively the needs of tomorrow. The result, a proposed "Institute Sabbatical Program," would focus on tenured department chairs deemed to warrant the major investment of time and resources inherent in this program, outlined below:

- From among department chairs approaching a sabbatical leave, selection will be made by a task force co-chaired by the medical school dean and the hospital's CEO. It could include relevant physicians and other scholars from the school, hospital, and elsewhere.
- Selection will be based upon criteria related to a candidate's performance in all aspects of department leadership. These will have been defined previously by medical school/hospital leadership, updated annually, and made known to all faculty after each annual review.
- Early in the year preceding the selected individual's sabbatical leave, a detailed review of his/her department will take place considering all aspects of scholarship, leadership, and management, actual practice in the areas of clinical care, teaching, re-

search, community service, patient satisfaction, and both overall academic achievement and individual advancement among department members. Departmental space, its efficient use, staffing, equipment, operating and business management, and other relevant indices will be considered.

- An external team of relevant experts will be gathered to spend time at the hospital to examine in detail these aspects of the department, having prepared in advance by reviewing a report produced by its chair to convey his/her view of the department's history, current strengths and weaknesses, and prospects for the future. The visiting team will inform themselves of insights, strengths, and advances at the department and at other institutions, along with other relevant developments and projections. Their written report — evaluating the department and its chair, and projecting its desirable future — will be shared with the department chair before he/she departs for the leave, and with medical school dean and hospital CEO.

- During the actual leave, in fulfilment of one of its primary functions and in anticipation of personal growth, the selected individual will undertake serious study in an area of his/her responsibility. He/she will also commit that on return, to remain as department chair for at least five years once mutual agreement as described below has been achieved.

- From timely consideration of the external review, and from personal knowledge and further inquiry, the selected individual would develop a plan for his/her department for the next five to ten years. At about six months in the year-long leave, he/she will return to present the dean/hospital CEO with the plan, including a detailed proposal for departmental rejuvenation. This proposal should be comparable to what would be expected from a potential candidate being recruited for department chairmanship as if the position were currently vacant.

- Starting with that proposal, the proposer and dean/hospital CEO would negotiate until they agreed on what will be done, timing of its components, and how financed (in major part from funds allocated for this specific sabbatical leave program but also including research grants existing and anticipated, clinical revenues, other potential charitable sources and other medical school, hospital resources, etc.). With the new vision and an agreed-upon program including funding for its implementation, the chairperson's remaining months of leave would allow further thought and action on both personal scholarship and program implementation. On return he/she would have enjoyed the intellectual renewal anticipated for a sabbatical leave and secured the comfort of committed plans for department strength and growth.

This Institute Sabbatical Program offers an imaginative and periodic opportunity to reinvigorate today's academic departments of excellence. It is indeed expensive, but the loss of a chairperson of surpassing ability or the potential of a slide into mediocrity may be equally costly or more so. A conservative estimate would suggest such a program no more frequently than one annually, with its implementation to follow over the subsequent three years or so. With some variation, there are about ten or twelve major clinical departments in most academic health centers—medicine, surgery, anesthesia, obstetrics/gynecology, pediatrics, psychiatry, pathology, radiology, neurology, orthopedics, radiation oncology, dermatology. Outstanding nursing leadership should be included and basic science departments in the hospital or medical school. The opportunity should stimulate diligence; it is not intended for every chair anticipating a sabbatical leave. Some chairs may be at the point of retirement; others unable to meet the program's high standard for inclusion.

Each specific instance of this program would require:

- Resources for the external review body, including for gathering needed information, visiting the department, and for preparation and delivery of its report.

- Adequate resources for the candidate's year of leave. Institutional support may vary, e.g., full salary for six months, or half-salary for twelve, but often is not sufficient for all reasonable needs of the individual for his/her program of personal scholarship and relative freedom from personal financial concerns arising out of being away for a full year — the need to get back even more often than the one dictated by the program, the added personal tax implications of income from renting one's house while away, etc.
- The largest component — resources to implement the new vision mutually agreed upon by the chairperson and the medical school/hospital leadership.

Bold in concept, this Institute Sabbatical Program would demand a designated endowment estimated now upward of $800 million or more. Its benefits would include the institution's unique attractiveness to academicians of the highest scholarship, clinical and research capability, vision, leadership, planning ability, and personal characteristics. Advantages would accrue in recruitment of excellent faculty, fellows and residents, helping strengthen the impressive performance the program anticipates.

My thoughts on this proposal offered a memorable opportunity some years ago. Like many in the Eastern United States, our hospital annually convened a few supporters enjoying the winter season in Florida. I was there at one such session to update our "BI family" on the hospital's progress, and of course, encourage continuing financial support. One of our guests invited me to accompany him back to Boston on his corporate jet. Midway in the flight, we started chatting. At 30,000 feet and standing behind pilot and copilot, we took advantage of a crystal-clear day to view Baltimore, Philadelphia, and New York City all at once. Long vistas prompt me to think about the future, so this became a time, I felt, to share this vision of my sabbatical proposal. My host thought it fascinating but unfortunately went no further despite my gentle but straightforward ask. I'm still looking for an angel with the megabucks to pull it off for BIDMC.

The challenges facing academic medicine are serious and growing. Pressures on both service and scholarship threaten the excellence of medicine, health care, community service, and the underlying science. A bold approach is needed, and while the Institute Sabbatical Program will neither resolve all problems nor allow universal implementation, an institution taking it on could lead the way.

CHAPTER 7: AFTERWORD

Among the most insightful writers on management I've come across is the late Peter Drucker. The clarity and acuity of his observations are appealing. Among Drucker's comments, I first came across his thoughts clarifying the concept of profit at a not-for-profit institution, such as our hospital. It was an issue sometimes raising questions from a board member or others.

"An enterprise that earns less on the total amount of money in the business than the going rate for capital is by definition operating at a deficit and stealing from the future. Everybody accepts this for the farmer who eats up the seed corn needed for next year's sowing... Everyone knows that the farmer's seed corn is not profit, even though it is surplus. But no one — including business executives — grasps that the 'profit' reported in company statements is not profit either; it is 'seed corn.' It is the cost of staying in business — an actual and genuine, albeit deferred cost."[32]

At a meeting in London years ago, I shared a speaker's platform with Peter Drucker. As the session concluded and the room emptied, he and his wife remained along with my wife and me. We invited them to join us for dinner, and it became the start of our friendship.

---

[32] Drucker PD. Managing in Turbulent Times. New York, NY: Harper Collins Publishers, Inc., 1980.

Periodically Mr. Drucker lectured at neighboring MIT in Cambridge, and we would touch base there. He became interested in what was taking place at Boston's Beth Israel Hospital. Later he invited my wife and me to a gathering at the Peter F. Drucker Graduate School of Management in Claremont, California, where he led an informal two-day discussion among a few guests one of whom was A. G. Lafley, an outstanding executive then chairman, president and CEO of Procter and Gamble. I mentioned to Mr. Lafley that I didn't understand the mission of P & G. "You manufacture soap and you sell Pringles and gobs of other things seeming unrelated. That doesn't tend to make for a unified mission statement." He replied, "It does. We make things better for the homemaker." I never forgot that.

Should we proclaim, "We make things better for the patient?" I don't think so. That wouldn't differentiate Beth Israel from other excellent hospitals in Boston and elsewhere. Beyond the high technical quality of our medical care, we focus on its warmth and personalization, the professionalism, and superlative nature of our nursing care, the understanding by other staff on their respective roles in service to patients, participative involvement of our patients, and the infusion of scholarship into our care to keep it at the leading edge. These may help differentiate us, but such virtues seem less convincing if the hospital touts them than when one patient tells others about their own care with us.

Among the insights of Mr. Drucker's, I found relevant for both management and governance his project, "The Five Most Important Questions You Will Ever Ask About Your Nonprofit Organization." This was amplified in a workbook dated 1993 by the Peter F. Drucker Foundation for Nonprofit Management.[33] The five questions are:

- What is our business (mission)?
- Who is our customer?
- What does the customer value?

---

[33] Drucker PD. The Five Most Important Questions You Will Ever Ask About Your Nonprofit Organization. San Francisco, CA: Jossey-Bass, Inc. Publishers, 1993.

- What have been our results?
- What is our plan?

What is our business (mission)?

"... a mission statement has to be operational...to focus on what the organization is in business to do so that everyone in the organization can say, 'This is my contribution to the goal.'...the task of the nonprofit leader is to try to translate the organization's mission statement into specifics...*to know what this organization is really trying to do*, why you are working, why you are asking for money, why you are asking for volunteers, what it is you want to achieve. *And the emphasis is on achievement.*"

Who is our customer?

"Everyone has more than one customer, if you define customers as *people who have the choice to accept or reject your services.*" We considered as "customers" not only patients, our primary customers, and their families but also our medical staff, all employees and trainees, our volunteers including board members, our donors, the wider community we try to serve, and Harvard Medical School and Harvard University. All have the choice to accept or reject us; we must work to satisfy them all. That calls for thoughtful balancing of priorities on our part.

What does the customer value?

"Value may be defined as quality or price, but you must keep in mind that the customer never buys a product. By definition the customer buys the satisfaction of a want... You must consider the needs of different types of people within the organization you are serving...only when you know what *each group* values can you set objectives based on their respective needs." And since both the demography of customers and the nature of their wants may change over time, figuring out what each considers to be of value becomes a continual requirement.

What have been our results?

"Performance is the ultimate test of any institution." Having defined what specific results relate to the organization's mission and its customers, measuring and monitoring those results are critical. For different categories of the organization's 'customers,' the extent of fulfilment of needs of each must be measured and the results re-examined periodically."

What is our plan?

"The primary results of a nonprofit institution are always outside the organization," Drucker argues. "Results are achieved by concentration, not by splintering." It's a challenge for the academic teaching hospital, with multiple missions that include clinical care of high quality, warmth and personalization in the treatment of both patients and staff, teaching medical students, training young physicians: maintaining continuing competence and content awareness among all medical and nursing professionals and other staff as well, biomedical research with its transfer to bedside diagnosis and treatment, and hospital-medical school relationships. Adding to that are control of costs, care of the indigent, and a focus on health and prevention of illness in the hospital's community. The task is huge and made more so in the evolving world of medical knowledge and complexity and that of competing economic pressures.

Priorities must be set and, unlike the situation for some organizations that may abandon a function for which they harbor less than ideal competence or are losing money, it is not always possible for the hospital. Peter Drucker suggests these questions to help focus on priorities:

- If we weren't already doing this, if we were not already committed to this, would we start doing it now?
- Are we working in the right area? Do we need to change our focus?

He ends the exercise:

- What have we learned and what do we recommend?
- Where should we focus our efforts?
- What, if anything, should we do differently?
- What is our plan to achieve (the desired) results for the organization?

Drucker concludes, "But you must understand that no decision has been made until someone has been designated to carry it out. Someone has to be accountable with a work plan, a goal, and a deadline. Unless self-assessment generates action, you have wasted your time."

These thoughts are useful for any organization, not-for-profit or other.